CUB SCOUT FUN BOOK

BY FELICIE T. AND FELICIE C. KENOWER
in collaboration with Bill and Bernard Martin

BOY SCOUTS OF AMERICA

$1.00

HOW TO USE THIS BOOK

Here is a book of projects Cub Scouts like to do. You can do most of these projects alone with materials that you can find around home. Your dad may need to help you in some instances.

The satisfactory completion of most of these activities will earn arrow point credits. The projects follow the program of electives for earning arrow point credits, listed in your Cub Scout handbook.

1960 PRINTING

Copyright 1956 by
BOY SCOUTS OF AMERICA
New Brunswick
New Jersey

No. 3720   40M960

CONTENTS

Hurricane Lamps Are Easily Made 4
How Strong Is Air? 6
Snowflake Cutouts 8
Hot Dog! Look at This Wiener Stick 10
Popgun Fun 12
Make a Recipe Holder 14
Mirror Magic—a Secret Code 16
The Bicycle Trail 18
Game Boards 20
Log Cabin Cinnamon Toast 21
How to Make a High-Flying Kite 22
Stick Puppets 24
A Puppet Play 26
Graham-Cracker Fort 28
The Secret Code Wheel 30
Surprise Eggs 32
Indian Color Puzzle 34
Indian Symbols 36
A Magic Ring of Paper 38
A "Guess Who" Greeting Card 40
Flying Saucer Kite 42
The Three-in-One Storyteller 44
Make Electricity 46
How to Make a Weather Vane 48
Wishing Boats 52
Finger Puppets 54
Photograph a Leaf without a Camera . . . 56
How to Make a Small Greenhouse 58
Make a Catapult to Launch a Parachute . . . 60
A Billboard Sign of Safety 62
Jigsaw Puzzle Greeting Card 64
Pirate Gold 66
How to Make a Rain Gauge 68
Bird Feeders 70
An Airplane with Lifting Power 72
How to Make a Tambourine 76
A Shadow Puppet 78
A Flying Fish for Kite Fans 80
Star Tricks 83
Make Water Rise into a Glass 84
The Betsy Ross Star 86
Button Button 88
Boomerang! Boomerang! 90
A Spinning Color Wheel 92
Fun with an Ant House 94

Hurricane Lamps Are Easily Made

YOU WILL NEED

A saw
A candle
A sharp knife
A ½ cup of flour
A hammer and a nail
A broomstick or long stick of wood
A tuna fish can (a No. 1 flat can)
A medium-sized screw and a screw driver
A small jar that fits inside the tuna fish can

SMALL PICKLE OR RELISH JAR

CANDLE

BALL OF FLOUR AND WATER PASTE

1.

Mix a half cup of flour with water to make a thick paste. Drop the ball of paste into the bottom of a small jar and set a candle in it. Allow the paste to dry thoroughly.

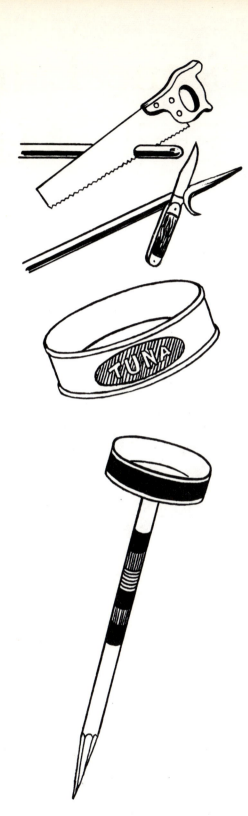

2.

Saw off the top of a broomstick to make a flat-top surface. Then, with a sharp knife whittle the other end of the stick to a point.

3.

Ask your mother for a flat tuna fish can open at one end. With a hammer, pound down any rough edge along the top of the can.

4.

Use a hammer and a nail to punch a hole in the bottom center of the can and then screw the can to the top of the broomstick.

5.

Paint and decorate the lamp holder. You can paint a narrow band of color around the rim of the candle jar if you want the jar to match the holder.

6.

Punch the holder into the ground and set the candle jar in the holder. This simple-to-make hurricane lamp gives a friendly light for nighttime picnics and back-yard gatherings.

EARN A WOLF ARROW POINT CREDIT in Handicraft, Elective 3, by making a hurricane lamp and holder to be used out-of-doors at night.

How Strong Is Air?

By working this experiment, you can test the strength of the air around you. Work at the sink so that it won't matter if you spill any water.

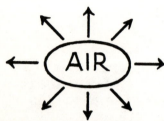

Air exerts strength in all directions: up, down, and to all sides.

1.

Fill a glass with water. Place cardboard on top of the glass. When turning the glass over, hold the cardboard snugly against the glass.

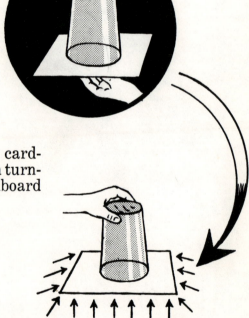

2.

Turn glass upside down, then let go of cardboard. The air pressing against the cardboard holds water in the glass.

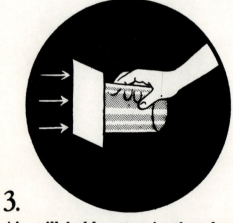

3.

Air will hold water in the glass, no matter which way you turn the glass.

YOU WILL NEED
A water glass
Several squares of cardboard

4.

It still works when the glass is only half full of water.

5.

When the glass is empty, the cardboard falls.

WHY?

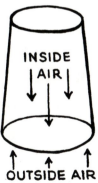

INSIDE AIR

OUTSIDE AIR

WHY?
Because the air inside the glass has as much strength as the air outside the glass. Therefore, the cardboard yields to the pull of gravity.

Snowflake Cutouts

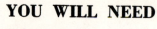

YOU WILL NEED

Scissors
A small plate
Sheets of white or colored paper

1.

Use a small plate to draw a circle on a sheet of white paper. Cut out the circle.

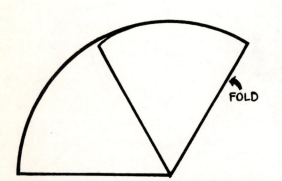

2.

First, fold the circle in half (Figure 1). Then fold the half circle into thirds (Figures 2 and 3).

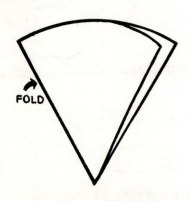

3.

Cut a jagged line design as shown in Figure 4. Now unfold the paper carefully.

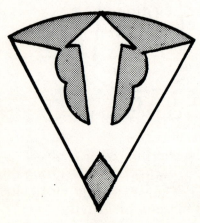

4.

Try other patterns for making snowflakes. It is easy to work out new designs.

**EARN AN ARROW
POINT CREDIT**
in Elective 10 by making paper snow-flakes to use for decorations on gift packages, for table favors, or for Christmas windows.

Hot Dog!

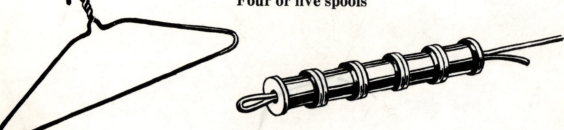

YOU WILL NEED

A pair of pliers
A wire coat hanger
Four or five spools

1.

Straighten out a wire coat hanger—the lighter the wire the better. Dad may have to help you untwist the wire.

2.

Use spools and pliers to make a handle on one end of the wire. The handle should be made long enough to fit comfortably into your hand.

3.

Sandpaper the point of the wiener stick or hold it in a fire long enough to burn off the paint. Then jab the point into the ground to polish it.

4.

Be sure the holder is long enough so that you can stand back from the fire when using it.

Look at This Wiener Stick!

EARN A WOLF OR LION ARROW POINT CREDIT in Elective 3 by making a wiener stick from a wire coat hanger.

Everybody likes a good wiener stick for picnics. Ask your dad to help you make one for each member of your family. Store the sticks on a nail in the basement or garage. They can be used year after year.

Popgun Fun

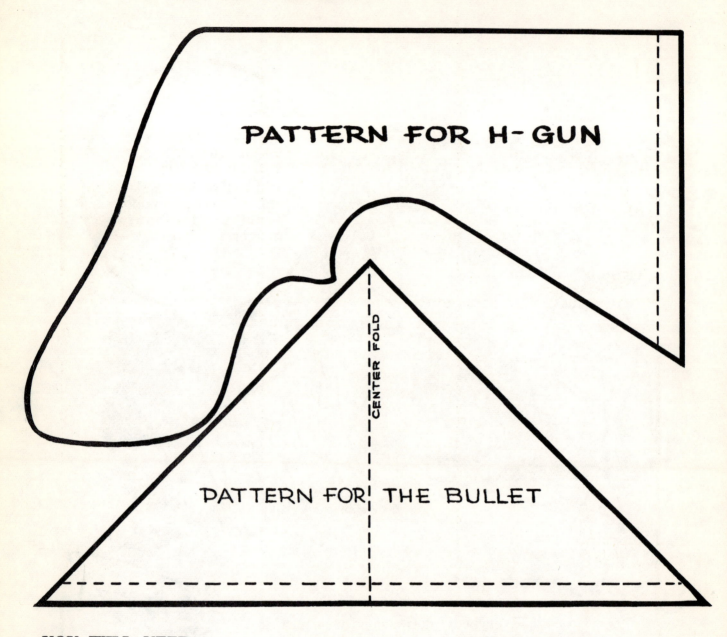

PATTERN FOR H-GUN

CENTER FOLD

PATTERN FOR THE BULLET

YOU WILL NEED

Ruler
Paste
Scissors
Pencil
A piece of light cardboard 8½ by 10 inches
A piece of thin paper (paper sack or laundry paper)

These two patterns are needed for making a "Hydrogen" Popgun. Trace patterns on another sheet of paper and use your tracings for cutout patterns.

12

**EARN A WOLF ARROW
POINT CREDIT**
in Parties and Gifts, Elective 10, by
making a popgun and giving it to
someone.

1. Draw a double pattern of the gun on a piece of cardboard.

2. Cut it out.

3. With a ruler and the tip of the scissors, crease along the center dotted line.

4. Fold the gun in the middle with the dotted lines to the outside.

5. Cut a triangular "bullet" pattern from a sheet of thin paper.

6. Paste along dotted line on "bullet."

7. Paste "bullet" to gun.

8. When dry fold the triangle into the gun.

9. Grasp the gun easily and swing downward to make it pop.

POP

Make a Recipe Holder

YOU WILL NEED

Sandpaper
Screw driver
Two small screws
A clip clothespin
A small hand drill or a brace and bit
A meat skewer or round stick about 6 inches long
A scrap of plywood or orange-crate wood, 5 by 6 inches

1.

Sandpaper the piece of plywood or orange crating until smooth. Wrap the sandpaper around a block of wood to make the sanding easier.

2.

Drill a hole a little smaller than the meat skewer (or round stick) in the top center of the board. Make the hole on a slant so your board will stand up as pictured.

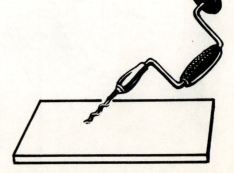

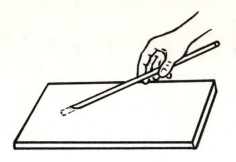

3.

Sandpaper the end of the stick so it will fit snugly in the hole. Lay the stick aside to be fitted into the hole the very last thing.

4.

Slip the spring off a clip clothespin and *save* all three parts—the two wooden pieces and the wire spring.

5.

Use two small screws to fasten one wooden section of the clothespin to the bottom center of the board, as pictured here.

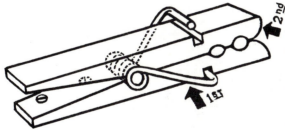

6.

Now put the clothespin back together in this manner: First, slip the wire spring around the wooden part of the clothespin that is fastened to the board. Then slip the second wooden part of the pin into the spring.

7.

Fit the round stick into the hole, now, and your recipe holder is ready for painting. You can use paint, stain, or shellac.

8.

If you are making the holder as a gift, write "Recipe Holder" on a card and slip it in the clothespin, so the person getting it will know how to use it.

EARN A WOLF OR LION ARROW POINT CREDIT
in **Elective 3** by **making a recipe holder for mom to use in the kitchen.**

Mirror Magic—

Can you read these messages written in mirror-magic code? It looks confusing but you should be able to figure it out in two minutes. A hint on the best way to read the code is in the title, "Mirror Magic."

THE LAW OF THE PACK

THE CUB SCOUT FOLLOWS
AKELA
THE CUB SCOUT HELPS THE
PACK GO
THE PACK HELPS THE CUB
SCOUT GROW
THE CUB SCOUT GIVES
GOOD WILL

The treasure is hidden in
the old hollow tree.

A Secret Code

EARN A WOLF ARROW POINT CREDIT in Secret Codes, Elective 1, by learning to read and write mirror-magic code.

YOU WILL NEED

A pencil
A mirror
Two sheets of writing paper
A sheet of carbon paper
Two paper clips or common pins

1. Lay out a sheet of carbon paper, carbon side up.

2. Cover it with two sheets of writing paper.

3. Fasten the three sheets of paper together with a paper clip or pin.

4. Write your message on the top sheet of writing paper.

5. The message in code will appear on the back side of the second sheet of writing paper.

6. To read the code, hold the coded message in front of a mirror.

17

The Bicycle Trail

INSTRUCTIONS

1.

The object of this game for two or more players is to make a trip from "home" to the "park."

2.

The rider who gets to the "park" first wins the game.

3.

Each player uses a bean or small button for his marker.

4.

All players start at the space marked "home." Players take turns.

5.

To determine the number of spaces to move forward, a player holds a pencil (with the eraser end down) above the "bicycle wheel." Closing his eyes, the player circles the pencil above the wheel, then brings the pencil down until it touches the wheel. The number on which the pencil lands tells the number of spaces the player moves his marker. If the pencil lands outside the "bicycle wheel" or touches a line, the player tries again.

6.

Two or more markers may occupy the same space.

7.

A rider must not "speed" into the "park," but must arrive there on an even count.

EARN A WOLF ARROW POINT CREDIT
in Parties and Gifts, Elective 10, by making a game board of The Bicycle Trail and giving it to a friend. See page 20 for instructions.

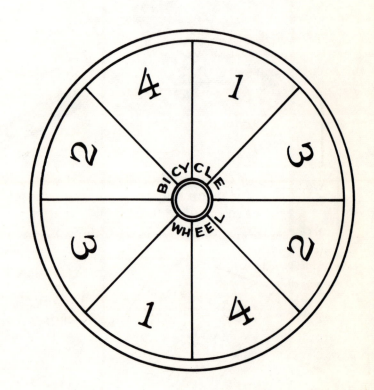

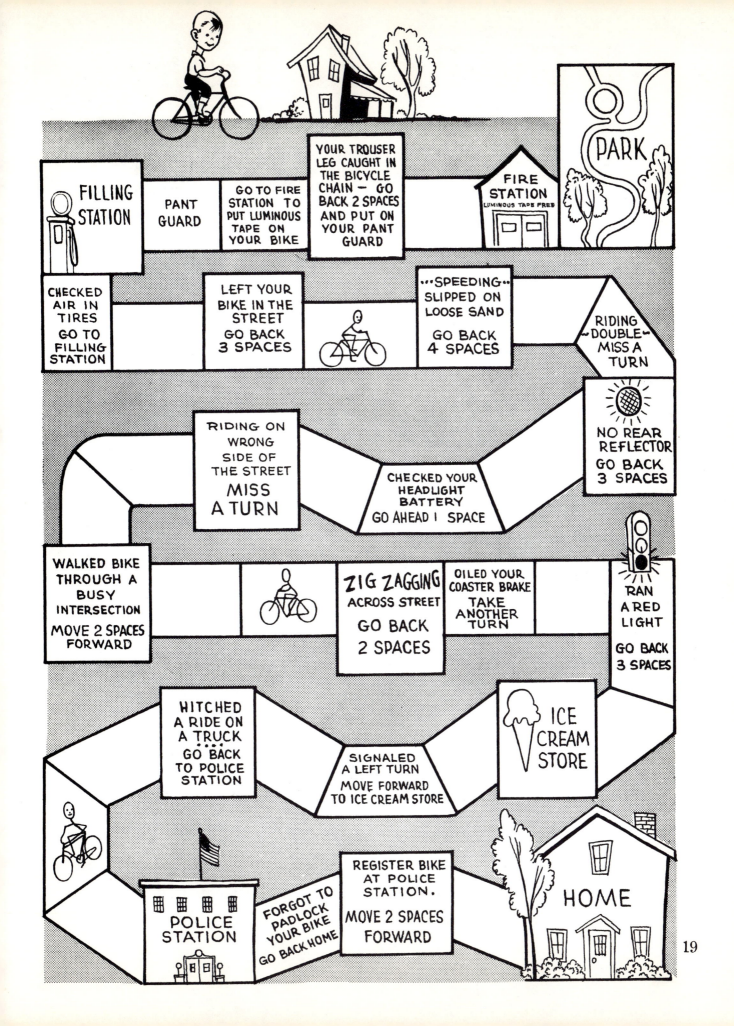

Game Boards

YOU WILL NEED

Scissors
Glue or paste
Clear shellac or varnish
A piece of cardboard or wood
at least 16 by 11 inches

1.

Carefully cut the Pirate Gold game found on pages 66 and 67.

2.

Cut out the title Pirate Gold and the instructions, and the map, leaving a good margin on each piece.

3.

Glue the title, the instructions, and the map to a large piece of heavy cardboard or wood. Decorate the game and the board with color if you wish.

4.

After the glue has thoroughly dried, coat the entire board with clear shellac or varnish to provide a hard finish.

EARN A WOLF ARROW POINT CREDIT
in Parties and Gifts, Elective 10, by making a game board and giving it to a friend or a member of your family.

5.

A similar game board can be made with The Bicycle Trail on pages 18 and 19.

Log Cabin Cinnamon Toast

YOU WILL NEED

A small plate
A saucedish
Two slices of bread
Four teaspoonfuls of sugar
One teaspoonful of cinnamon
A small pan with a handle
Two tablespoonfuls of butter or margarine

1.

After you have washed your hands and put on an apron, mix 4 teaspoonfuls of sugar and 1 teaspoonful of cinnamon in a saucedish. Stir it until well mixed.

2.

Melt 2 tablespoonfuls of butter in a small pan. Use a low fire.

3.

Toast two slices of bread and spread one side of each piece of toast with melted butter. Use a teaspoon to spread the melted butter.

4.

Sprinkle the buttered side of the toast with the cinnamon and sugar mixture.

5.

Cut each slice of toast in half. Then cut each half in half, making four strips from each piece of toast.

6.

Stack the eight strips in the shape of a log cabin. Serve on a small plate and eat while warm.

EARN A WOLF ARROW POINT CREDIT
in Cooking, Elective 19, by making log cabin cinnamon toast. It is a good after-school snack.

How to Make a High-Flying Kite

YOU WILL NEED

Two kite sticks
Ball of strong string
Sheet of strong, lightweight paper, 36 by 34 inches
Coping saw or single-edge razor blade
Scissors, pencil, and ruler
The white of an egg for pasting

Kite sticks must be lightweight and flexible—but strong. If you don't have kite sticks, you can purchase ⅛ inch dowel sticks or strips of flat, narrow screen molding at your lumberyard for 10 or 15 cents. A large laundry or dry-cleaning sack makes a good kite paper.

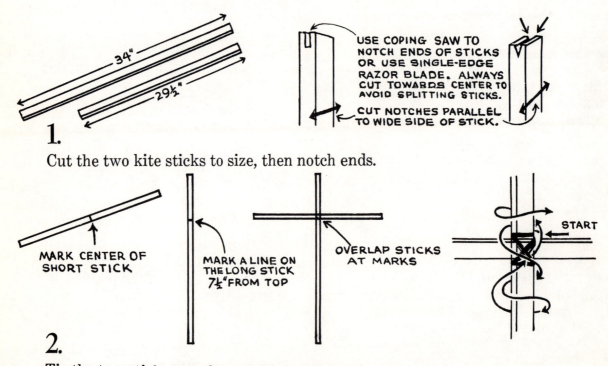

34"

29½"

USE COPING SAW TO NOTCH ENDS OF STICKS OR USE SINGLE-EDGE RAZOR BLADE. ALWAYS CUT TOWARDS CENTER TO AVOID SPLITTING STICKS.

CUT NOTCHES PARALLEL TO WIDE SIDE OF STICK.

1. Cut the two kite sticks to size, then notch ends.

MARK CENTER OF SHORT STICK

MARK A LINE ON THE LONG STICK 7½" FROM TOP

OVERLAP STICKS AT MARKS

START

2. Tie the two sticks together as shown here.

3. String outer edge of the kite frame, slipping string through notches at ends of sticks, then tie.

22

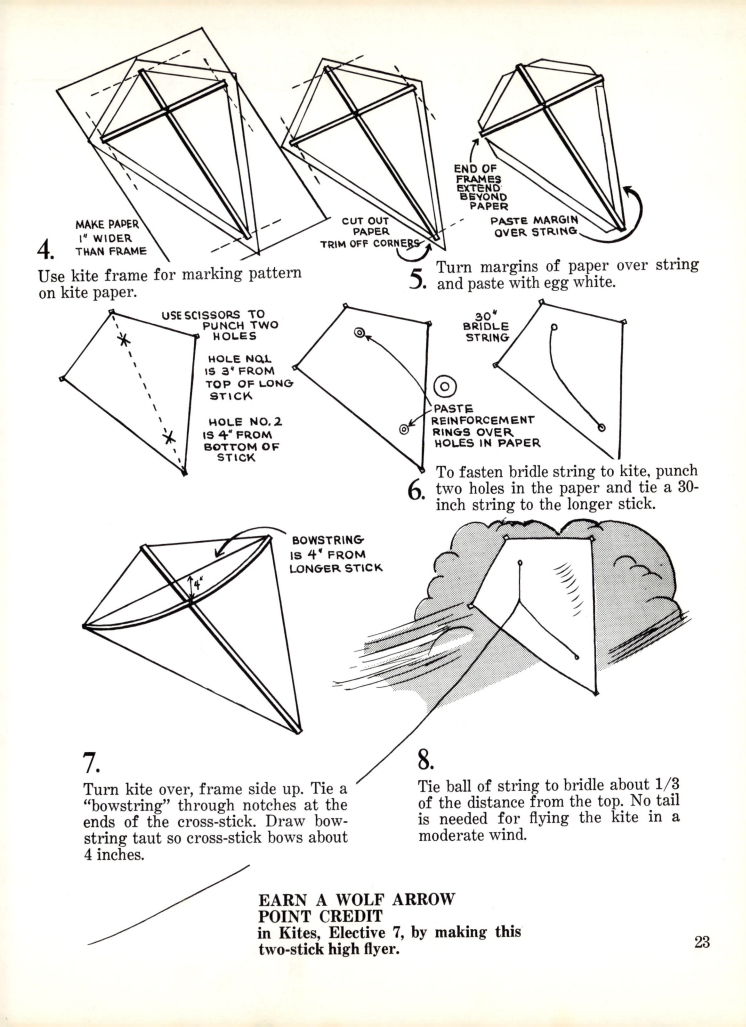

4.
Use kite frame for marking pattern on kite paper.

MAKE PAPER 1" WIDER THAN FRAME

CUT OUT PAPER TRIM OFF CORNERS

END OF FRAMES EXTEND BEYOND PAPER

PASTE MARGIN OVER STRING

5. Turn margins of paper over string and paste with egg white.

USE SCISSORS TO PUNCH TWO HOLES

HOLE NO. 1 IS 3" FROM TOP OF LONG STICK

HOLE NO. 2 IS 4" FROM BOTTOM OF STICK

PASTE REINFORCEMENT RINGS OVER HOLES IN PAPER

30" BRIDLE STRING

6. To fasten bridle string to kite, punch two holes in the paper and tie a 30-inch string to the longer stick.

BOWSTRING IS 4" FROM LONGER STICK

4"

7.
Turn kite over, frame side up. Tie a "bowstring" through notches at the ends of the cross-stick. Draw bowstring taut so cross-stick bows about 4 inches.

8.
Tie ball of string to bridle about 1/3 of the distance from the top. No tail is needed for flying the kite in a moderate wind.

EARN A WOLF ARROW POINT CREDIT in Kites, Elective 7, by making this two-stick high flyer.

Stick Puppets

YOU WILL NEED

Paste
Scissors
Cardboard
Crayons or paints
Tiny nails or strong glue
Four thin strips of wood about 12 inches long

1.

Cut out page of puppet figures and paste on lightweight cardboard. Place under a heavy book until dry. If you do not want to cut page 25 from your book, trace the puppet figures directly on the cardboard.

2.

Color or paint the puppets and cut them out. The safety flag Henry is holding should be colored green and yellow.

3.

Cut four strips of wood about ½ inch wide and 12 inches long from a piece of orange crate wood or other soft wood. Sandpaper until smooth.

4.

With thumbtacks, tiny nails, or strong glue, fasten each puppet to a strip of wood.

With these puppets you can present the puppet play on pages 26 and 27. Other puppet characters can be made from your own drawings or from pictures in magazines.

EARN A BEAR ARROW POINT CREDIT
in Shadow Plays, Elective 2, by making these paper puppets for the puppet play on pages 26 and 27.

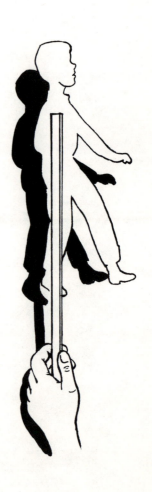

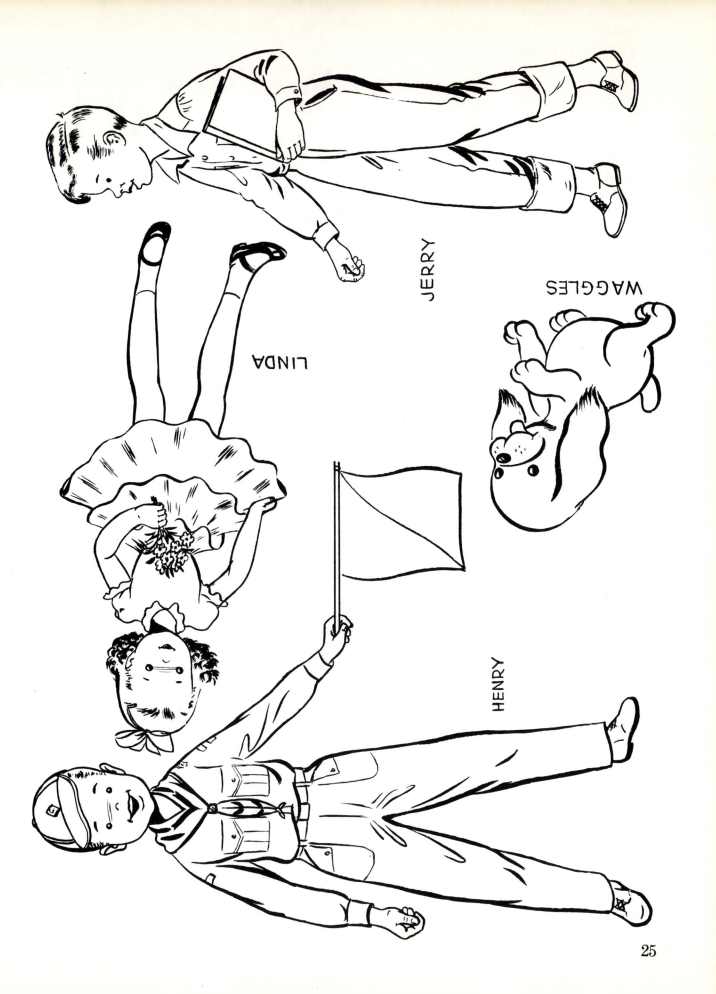

JERRY

WAGGLES

LINDA

HENRY

25

A Puppet Play

YOU WILL NEED

The stick puppets found on page 25

FRONT

BACK

SIMPLE TABLE DRAPED

CUT OUT BACK PORTION OF BOX

FRONT

PUPPETS SLIP UP THROUGH THIS HOLE

BOX SET ON TABLE

1.

This play may be presented using the end of a table for the stage. No background is needed.

2.

If you prefer, you can make a stage from a large cardboard box set on a table.

3.

Arrange the puppets on a chair or stand close to you so you can reach them easily while giving the show.

4.

Work one puppet with each hand.

5.

For best results, the play should be memorized; but if you wish, a friend can read the play while you work the puppets.

6.

Make the puppet jiggle a little when it is "talking." Practice in front of a mirror to learn to move your puppets in an interesting way.

7.

Change your voice when the different characters speak.

EARN A BEAR ARROW POINT CREDIT in Shadow Plays, Elective 2, by presenting this puppet play at school or den or pack meeting.

"Safety First"

(The scene is a corner near a schoolhouse. The time is 8:30 in the morning. Henry, the Safety Patrol, is on duty when the play begins.)

JERRY *(Runs in and asks breathlessly)*: Hey, has the bell rung? *(Jerry starts to run across the street.)*

HENRY: Wait a minute! There's a car coming!

JERRY *(Stops and returns to stand beside Henry)*: Oh, I didn't see it! Has the bell rung?

HENRY: Not yet, but even if it had, you shouldn't run across the street without looking. You're new here, aren't you?

JERRY: Sure, but how did you know?

HENRY: Kids at this school know that they shouldn't cross the street until the Safety Patrol gives the signal with his flag. Like this! *(Henry moves his safety flag, pointing it across the street.)* When the Safety Patrol blocks the sidewalk with the flag, like this *(He demonstrates with his flag)*, it means that you must wait on the sidewalk until the street is clear.

JERRY: That's baby stuff! I can look out for myself!

HENRY: It's safer when the Safety Patrol is here to help you. *(He moves his flag to let Jerry cross the street.)* The street is clear now. You can cross.

JERRY *(Crosses the street, then looks back toward Henry)*: Yeah! Yeah! Listen to the bossy Safety Patrol. Yeah! Yeah! *(He leaves, still shouting at Henry.)*

LINDA *(Enters on way to school)*: Hi! Henry!

HENRY: Hello, Linda. Wait until this car passes, then you can cross with my safety flag. *(He holds flag across the sidewalk.)*

LINDA: Who was that boy who was shouting at you just now?

HENRY: I don't know, Linda. He's new here.

LINDA: You ought to report him to the principal, Henry. He certainly was acting smarty.

HENRY: Oh, he's all right. As soon as he learns the safety signals, we won't have any trouble with him. He's probably just scared to death, coming to a new town and a new school and all.

LINDA: Maybe. I never thought of that.

HENRY: I don't mind his talk as long as he obeys the safety signals. It's my job to help him, that's all. *(Henry signals for Linda to cross.)* It's all clear now.

LINDA: Thanks, Henry. *(She crosses the street and leaves.)*

WAGGLES *(Enters, running after Linda)*: Bow-wow-wow-wow!

HENRY: Wait a minute, Waggles! You have to obey the safety rules too! *(Henry places his flag across the sidewalk and Waggles waits beside it.)*

WAGGLES: Bow-wow!

HENRY: Cars are just as dangerous to little dogs as they are to boys and girls.

WAGGLES: Bow-wow-wow-wow!

HENRY: Are you going to school, too, Waggles?

WAGGLES *(Barks sadly)*: Bow-wow-wow-wow!

HENRY: Then come on! There's the bell. Let's put the safety flag away! *(Both run off, Waggles barking as they go.)*

Graham-Cracker Fort

YOU WILL NEED
A small pan
Sixteen graham crackers
A small mixing bowl
1 teaspoonful of vanilla
1 cup of powdered sugar
1 tablespoonful of boiling water
1 level tablespoonful of butter or margarine

TO MAKE THE FROSTING

1.
Pour 1 cup of powdered sugar in a small mixing bowl.

2.
Melt 1 level tablespoonful of butter or margarine in a pan and add to the powdered sugar.

3.
Boil a little water (in the pan used for melting the butter). Add 1 tablespoonful of boiling water to the powdered sugar.

4.
Add 1 teaspoonful of vanilla to the powdered sugar.

5.
Stir powdered sugar mixture until smooth and creamy. Add a bit more water if mixture is too stiff.

TO MAKE THE SANDWICH-COOKIES

1.
Spread a graham cracker with frosting. Then stick another cracker lightly on top to make a sandwich-cookie.

2.
You'll have enough frosting for eight sandwich-cookies—and a little extra for spoon-lickers.

3.
Wrap the cookies in wax paper until time to serve.

TO MAKE THE FORT

1.

Stack the cookies on a plate in the shape of a fort.

2.

Decorate the plate with small flags and "warriors" from your toy chest.

EARN A WOLF OR BEAR ARROW POINT CREDIT in Cooking, Elective 19, by making a graham-cracker fort for a family snack or dessert.

The Secret Code Wheel

Here is a code wheel that you and your buddy can use to keep your messages absolutely secret. No one will ever figure out the coded messages unless he has the code wheel.

YOU WILL NEED

Paste
Scissors
Cardboard

1.

Cut out the code wheels and paste on cardboard. Place under a heavy book until dry. If you don't want to cut this page from your book, trace the code wheels directly on the cardboard.

2.

Cut out the circles and place the smaller circle marked "Key" on top of the larger circle.

3.

For your first message, turn the "Key" circle so that the number 15 is directly under the letter "A" on the larger circle. At the top of your message write "A-15" which explains the key to the code. Now write your message, using corresponding numbers instead of letters. "How are you?" would be written "22-3-11 15-6-19 13-3-9."

4.

On receiving your message, your buddy first sets his code wheel to "A-15" which is written on the top of your message. He then has the key for reading the coded message.

5.

Twenty-six different codes can be written by using the code wheel in various combinations of letters and numbers.

6.

Use your code wheel to read this message.

"A-13"   16-1   11-1-7-4   14-17-5-6

To Write A Code
Place "Key" Circle
Within This Circle

Substitute Numbers
For Letters

KEY

EARN A WOLF ARROW POINT CREDIT in Secret Codes, Elective 1, by making a secret code.

Surprise Eggs

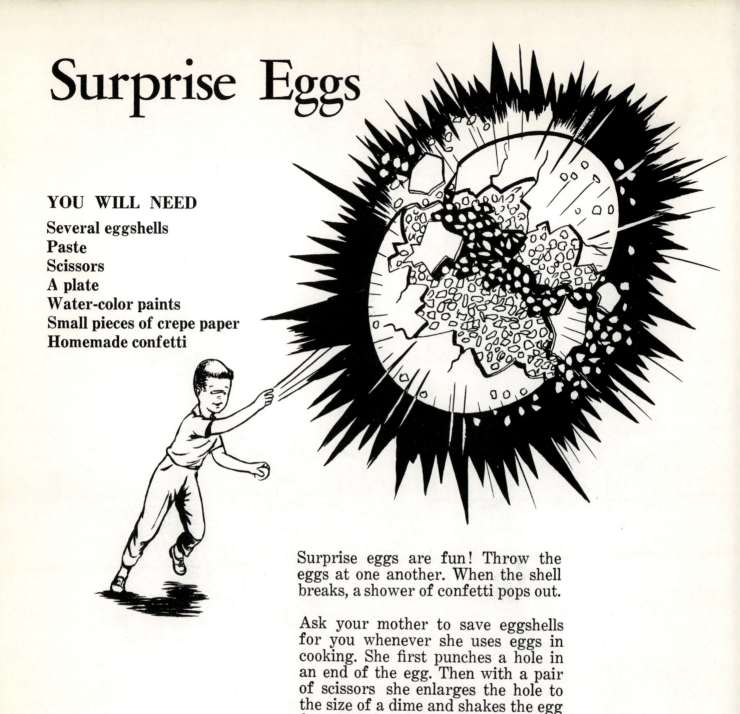

YOU WILL NEED

Several eggshells
Paste
Scissors
A plate
Water-color paints
Small pieces of crepe paper
Homemade confetti

Surprise eggs are fun! Throw the eggs at one another. When the shell breaks, a shower of confetti pops out.

Ask your mother to save eggshells for you whenever she uses eggs in cooking. She first punches a hole in an end of the egg. Then with a pair of scissors she enlarges the hole to the size of a dime and shakes the egg from the shell into a dish. Rinse the shell with water and let it dry.

EARN A BEAR ELECTIVE POINT CREDIT
in Party Spirit, Elective 10, by making surprise eggs as favors for a party.

1.

Pour a tablespoonful of confetti into the eggshell. Make confetti by cutting a magazine page into tiny scraps.

2.

Paste a piece of crepe paper about the size of a quarter over the hole in the eggshell.

3.

Paint the eggshell with water colors. The Indian symbols on page 36 in this book make attractive decorations.

4.

Try decorating another surprise egg with small colored seals or with tiny pictures cut from a magazine.

Indian Color Puzzle

YOU WILL NEED

Green, purple, and yellow pencils or crayons

PUZZLE: Color the squares from left to right as follows:

Row 1	9 green 4 green	4 yellow	5 green	1 purple	1 green	1 purple
Row 2	11 green 3 green	2 yellow	4 green	2 purple	1 green	2 purple
Row 3	10 green 1 green	1 yellow 3 purple	1 green 2 green	1 yellow	3 green	3 purple
Row 4	5 green 2 green	1 yellow 4 purple	3 green 1 green	1 yellow 4 purple	2 green 1 green	1 yellow
Row 5	4 green 6 green	1 yellow 4 purple	1 green 1 green	1 yellow 4 purple	1 green 1 green	1 yellow
Row 6	3 green	1 yellow	3 green	1 yellow	17 green	
Row 7	2 green	1 yellow	22 green			
Row 8	1 green	1 yellow	23 green			
Row 9	1 yellow 1 yellow	4 green 1 green	2 purple 1 yellow	9 green 4 green	1 yellow	1 green
Row 10	4 green 1 green	3 purple 1 yellow	9 green 4 green	1 yellow	1 green	1 yellow
Row 11	5 green	1 purple	10 green	5 yellow	4 green	
Row 12	11 purple	4 green	1 yellow	5 green	1 yellow	3 green
Row 13	11 purple	1 green	3 yellow	7 green	3 yellow	
Row 14	3 purple 1 yellow	2 green 7 green	1 purple 1 yellow	2 green 2 green	3 purple	3 green
Row 15	2 purple 3 yellow	2 green 3 green	3 purple 1 yellow	2 green 3 green	2 purple 3 yellow	1 green
Row 16	1 purple 1 yellow	2 green 7 green	5 purple 1 yellow	2 green 2 green	1 purple	3 green
Row 17	3 green	5 purple	4 green	3 yellow	7 green	3 yellow
Row 18	2 green 6 green	1 purple 1 yellow	2 green 5 green	1 purple 1 yellow	2 green 3 green	1 purple
Row 19	1 green 6 green	1 purple 5 yellow	2 green 4 green	3 purple	2 green	1 purple
Row 20	2 purple 1 yellow	1 green 1 green	5 purple 1 yellow	1 green 1 green	2 purple 1 yellow	5 green 4 green
Row 21	1 purple 1 yellow	1 green 1 green	7 purple 1 yellow	1 green 1 green	1 purple 1 yellow	5 green 4 green

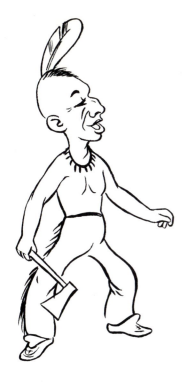

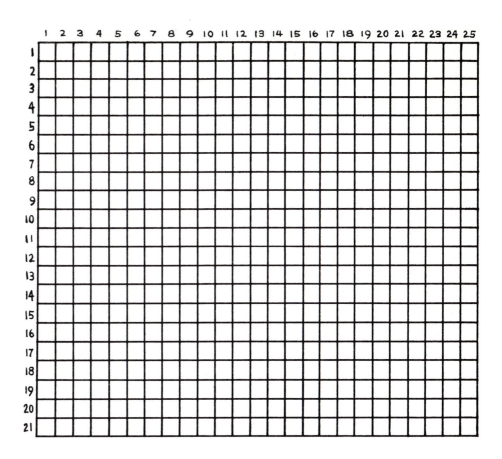

Hidden in the color puzzle are four Indian symbols. As you color the squares according to directions, the Indian symbols will appear. Identify the symbols by looking at the chart on page 36.

EARN A WOLF ARROW POINT CREDIT
in Drawing, Elective 13, by working this color puzzle and finding the hidden Indian symbols.

Indian Symbols

YOU WILL NEED

A pencil
Several sheets of paper

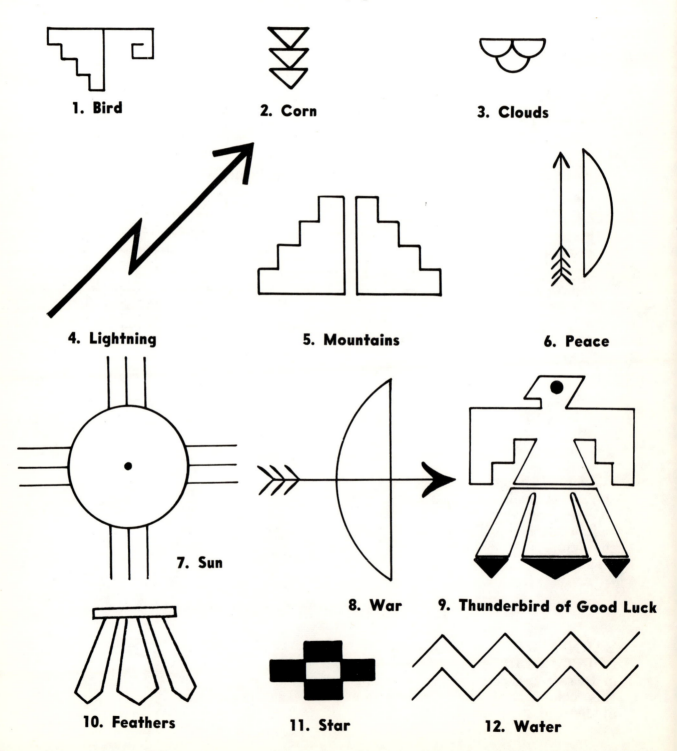

1. Bird

2. Corn

3. Clouds

4. Lightning

5. Mountains

6. Peace

7. Sun

8. War

9. Thunderbird of Good Luck

10. Feathers

11. Star

12. Water

Can you read the Indian symbols in this story of "The Hopi Indian Snake Dance"?

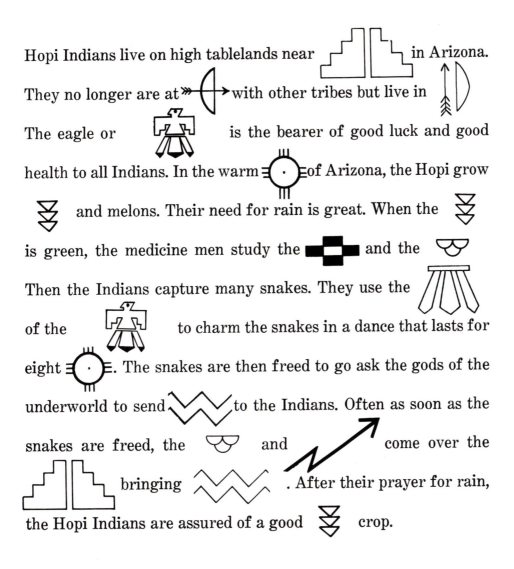

Hopi Indians live on high tablelands near ⌐⌐ in Arizona. They no longer are at ⟩⟩⟨→ with other tribes but live in ⫯. The eagle or 🦅 is the bearer of good luck and good health to all Indians. In the warm ☼ of Arizona, the Hopi grow ▽ and melons. Their need for rain is great. When the ▽ is green, the medicine men study the ▬ and the ⌣. Then the Indians capture many snakes. They use the ⋔ of the 🦅 to charm the snakes in a dance that lasts for eight ☼. The snakes are then freed to go ask the gods of the underworld to send ∿ to the Indians. Often as soon as the snakes are freed, the ⌣ and ↗ come over the ⌐⌐ bringing ∿∿. After their prayer for rain, the Hopi Indians are assured of a good ▽ crop.

EARN A BEAR ARROW POINT CREDIT
in Indian Signs, Elective 1, by drawing and knowing Indian symbols.

A Magic Ring of Paper

YOU WILL NEED

Paste
Scissors
A double sheet of newspaper

Do you want to be a magician? Here's a trick that is easy but puzzling. It will mystify your friends—and you, too!

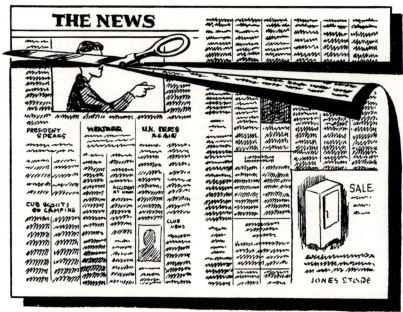

1.

Cut a 4-inch strip from the top of a double sheet of newspaper.

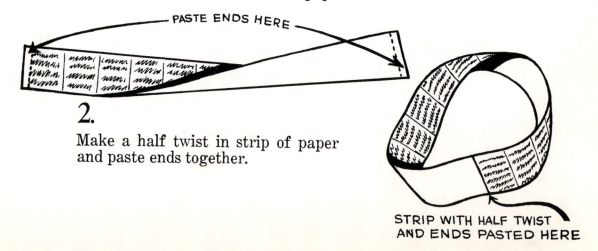

PASTE ENDS HERE

2.

Make a half twist in strip of paper and paste ends together.

STRIP WITH HALF TWIST AND ENDS PASTED HERE

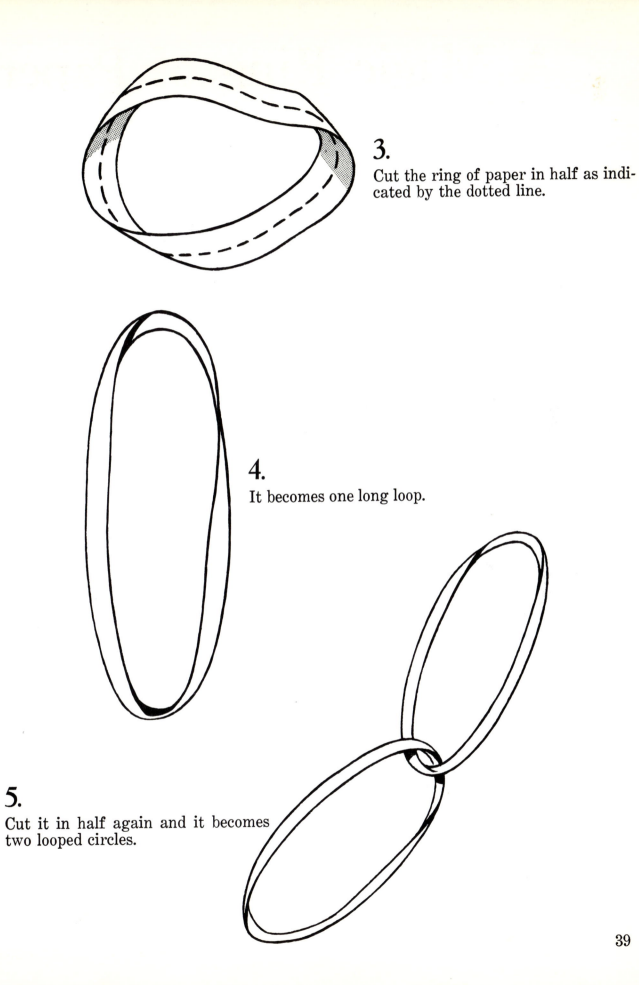

3.
Cut the ring of paper in half as indicated by the dotted line.

4.
It becomes one long loop.

5.
Cut it in half again and it becomes two looped circles.

A "Guess Who" Greeting Card

Everyone likes to receive a "mystery" card or letter, especially one like this. The letters sparkle and the mystery is fun. The directions may look hard, but the card is easy to make.

1.

Cut the head from a snapshot of yourself without damaging the rest of the photograph.

2.

Paste the head on a piece of colored paper a little smaller than the size of an envelope.

3.

With ink, sign the card: "I lost my head over you. Happy Birthday." Then sign your name.

4.

Mount the rest of the photograph on another piece of colored paper.

YOU WILL NEED

A plate
A pencil
A snapshot of yourself
Three tablespoonfuls of salt
A sheet of colored paper
A sheet of heavy white paper
Some of your mother's nail polish

5.

Now paste the snapshot on heavy white paper that is 1 inch higher and 3½ times wider than the snapshot.

6.

At the right of the snapshot, print lightly with a pencil "HAPPY BIRTHDAY."

7.

Now paint the letters, one by one, with nail polish.

8.

As you finish painting each letter with polish, sprinkle that letter with salt. This makes letters sparkle.

9.

When finished, use ink to sign the white card, "Guess Who?" Fold card to fit an envelope and mail to someone on his birthday.

10.

A day later mail the rest of the photograph (the head) so your friend will know who sent the first card.

EARN A WOLF ARROW POINT CREDIT
in Handicraft, Elective 3, by making this mystery card for someone's birthday.

Flying Saucer Kite

YOU WILL NEED

Lightweight paper sack from the dry cleaners
Pencil, ruler, paste, scissors, crayons
Fourteen-inch strip of kraft gummed tape, 3 inches wide
Four or five yards of lightweight string

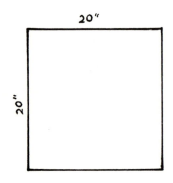
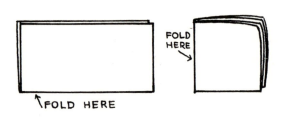

1.
Cut two 20-inch squares of lightweight brown paper, and fold each square into fourths, as shown here.

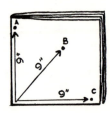
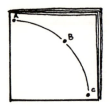

2.
From the folded corner of each paper, measure off 9 inches in the three positions shown above. Then, with a pencil, draw a circular line connecting points A, B, and C.

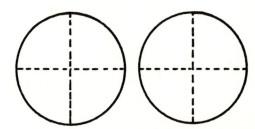

3.
Cut each sheet of paper along the pencil line. Now, unfold the fan-shaped pieces and you will have two 18-inch circles of paper.

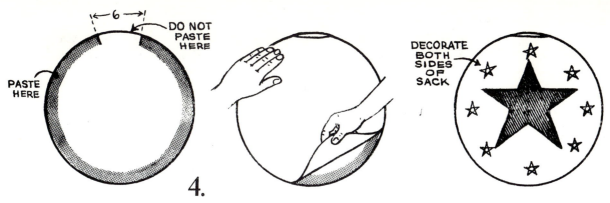

4.

Paste the two circles together as shown here, forming a round paper sack. Paint or color the sack with stars.

5.

Moisten a 14-inch strip of kraft gummed tape, 3 inches wide. (Sticky side to the outside), form a 5-inch circle of tape. Insert circle into the hole in the sack and glue it carefully into position.

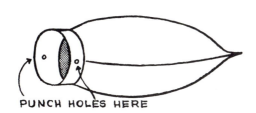

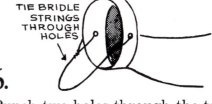

6.

Punch two holes through the tape as shown here. Tie a bridle string through the holes.

7.

Tie a small ball of string to the bridle string and the kite is ready to fly. It will not fly high, but when you run with it, it dives and whirls as no other kite will.

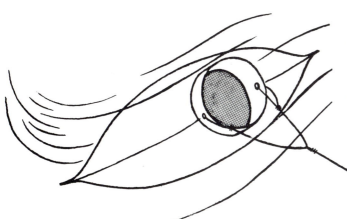

EARN A WOLF ARROW POINT CREDIT
in Kites, Elective 7, by making and flying this simple kite.

The Three-in-One Storyteller

1.

When the Cub Scout speaks, put on the Cub Scout cap and speak in your natural voice.

2.

When the den chief speaks, put on the Boy Scout cap and speak in a deep voice.

3.

When the Den Mother speaks, put on the woman's hat and speak in a very high voice.

4.

The story is funnier when you change hats quickly and speak rapidly. But be sure to speak clearly so everyone can understand what you are saying.

5.

Memorize the story. It isn't very long.

6.

Stand behind a low table as you tell the story. Place the hats on the table in front of you.

THE STORY

Ladies and gentlemen, three of us Cub Scouts were going to present a play for you tonight, but the other two boys haven't come. Therefore, I will have to take all the parts myself. The name of the play is "Cub Scout Inspection." The cast of characters is the Den Mother, the den chief, and Johnny, a Cub Scout, wearing one red and one blue sock. The scene is a Cub Scout den meeting. The Den Mother is speaking:

DEN MOTHER: Cubs, line up for inspection.

DEN CHIEF: They all look fine except Johnny.

JOHNNY: Me?

DEN MOTHER: Johnny?

DEN CHIEF: Yes, Johnny.

JOHNNY: What's wrong with me?

DEN MOTHER: What's wrong with him?

DEN CHIEF: Look at his socks.

JOHNNY: My socks?

DEN MOTHER: His socks?

DEN CHIEF: Your socks.

DEN MOTHER: Why Johnny, you have on one red sock . . .

DEN CHIEF: . . . and one blue sock.

JOHNNY: One red sock?

DEN CHIEF: Yes, and one blue sock.

JOHNNY: That's funny.

DEN CHIEF: What's funny?

DEN MOTHER: What's funny?

JOHNNY: I have another pair at home just like them.

THE END

EARN A WOLF ARROW POINT CREDIT in Make Believe, Elective 2, by acting out this three-in-one story for your den or pack meeting.

Make Electricity

By rubbing two unlike objects together, you can produce a type of
electricity known as static electricity.
It will not shock you or hurt you. By
doing the four experiments on this
page, you will learn some of the ways
that static electricity is produced.

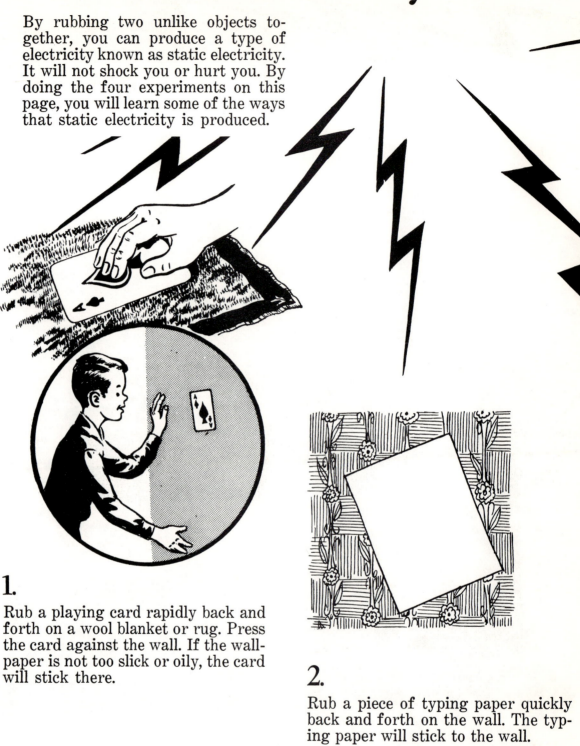

1.

Rub a playing card rapidly back and
forth on a wool blanket or rug. Press
the card against the wall. If the wall-
paper is not too slick or oily, the card
will stick there.

2.

Rub a piece of typing paper quickly
back and forth on the wall. The typing paper will stick to the wall.

3.

Comb your hair briskly with a dry comb. Hold the comb close to your hair and see how the static electricity draws the ends of the hair up to the comb. If your hair is wet or oily, this experiment will not work.

4.

Briskly comb your hair with a dry comb and touch it to a small piece of tissue paper. The tissue paper will stick to the comb.

YOU WILL NEED

A comb
A sheet of typing paper
A playing card (not plastic)
A piece of tissue paper or cleansing tissue

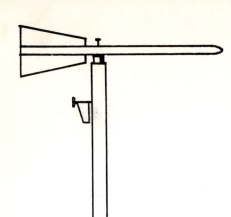

How to Make a Weather Vane

A successful weather vane must be well balanced, must revolve easily, and have a well-marked indicator for showing true north. This weather vane is easily made, but you may need dad's help in cutting the tin pieces.

YOU WILL NEED

A broom handle
A small nut
Some four-penny nails
The stick out of an old window shade
Adhesive tape
Small brads
No. 2 tin can, or a piece of tin
Tin snips or heavy scissors
Pieces of scrap wood
Hammer, saw, pliers

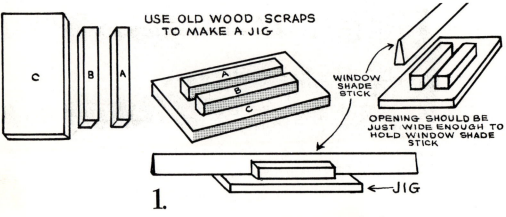

USE OLD WOOD SCRAPS TO MAKE A JIG

WINDOW SHADE STICK

OPENING SHOULD BE JUST WIDE ENOUGH TO HOLD WINDOW SHADE STICK

← JIG

1.

First, make the jig pictured above. The jig is a wooden frame used for holding the window-shade stick as you work with it. The jig takes only a few minutes to make, but it will save much time in making the weather vane.

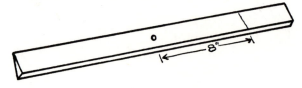

2.

Mark a line 8 inches from the rivet in the center of the window-shade stick. Now set the stick in the jig and saw the stick in two at the pencil mark.

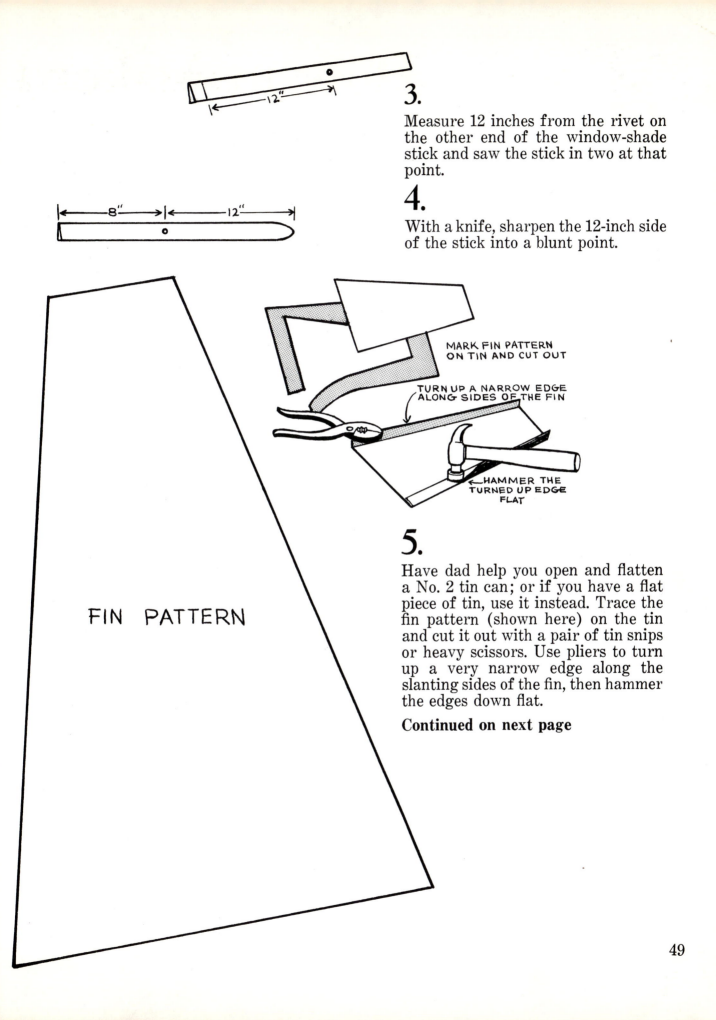

3.

Measure 12 inches from the rivet on the other end of the window-shade stick and saw the stick in two at that point.

4.

With a knife, sharpen the 12-inch side of the stick into a blunt point.

MARK FIN PATTERN ON TIN AND CUT OUT

TURN UP A NARROW EDGE ALONG SIDES OF THE FIN

HAMMER THE TURNED UP EDGE FLAT

5.

Have dad help you open and flatten a No. 2 tin can; or if you have a flat piece of tin, use it instead. Trace the fin pattern (shown here) on the tin and cut it out with a pair of tin snips or heavy scissors. Use pliers to turn up a very narrow edge along the slanting sides of the fin, then hammer the edges down flat.

Continued on next page

FIN PATTERN

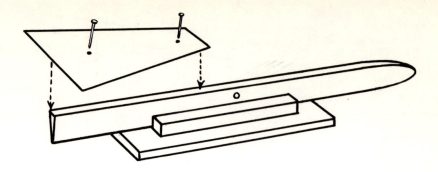

6.

Place the window-shade stick in the jig with the wide edge of the stick on top. Center the fin on the 8-inch end of the stick and nail it fast. Use very small (No. 8) brads or nails, or the wood might split.

TWO ENDS MUST BALANCE

7.

At the 12-inch end of the stick, tape enough small nails to the narrow edge to balance the stick as pictured.

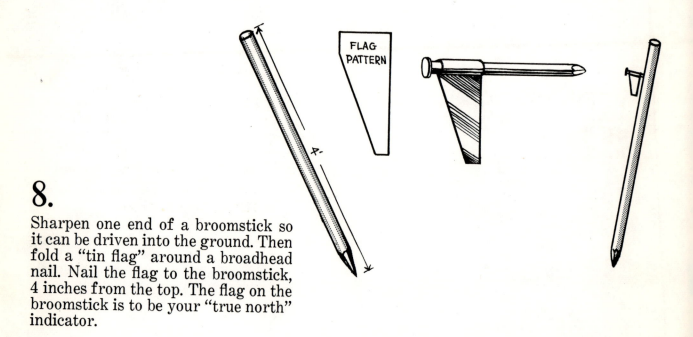

FLAG PATTERN

8.

Sharpen one end of a broomstick so it can be driven into the ground. Then fold a "tin flag" around a broadhead nail. Nail the flag to the broomstick, 4 inches from the top. The flag on the broomstick is to be your "true north" indicator.

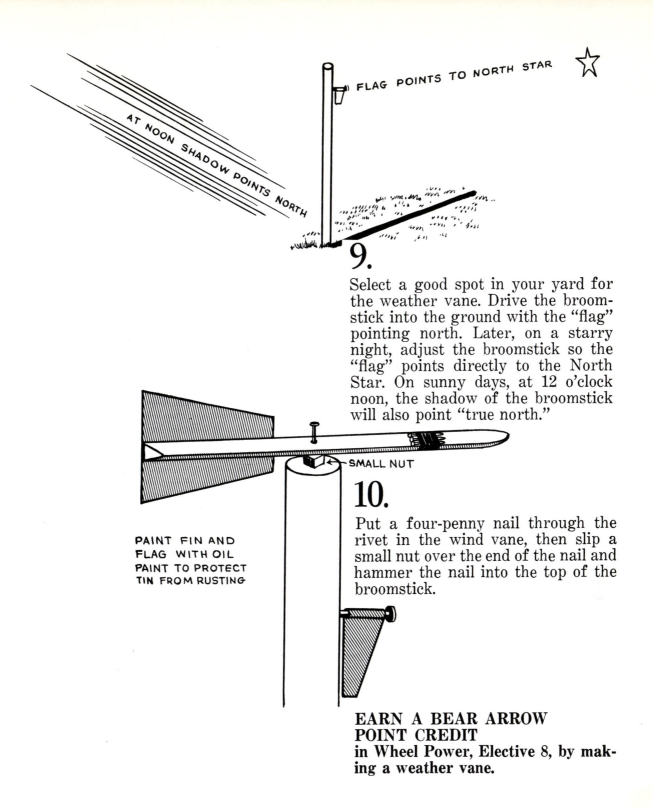

FLAG POINTS TO NORTH STAR

AT NOON SHADOW POINTS NORTH

9.

Select a good spot in your yard for the weather vane. Drive the broomstick into the ground with the "flag" pointing north. Later, on a starry night, adjust the broomstick so the "flag" points directly to the North Star. On sunny days, at 12 o'clock noon, the shadow of the broomstick will also point "true north."

SMALL NUT

PAINT FIN AND FLAG WITH OIL PAINT TO PROTECT TIN FROM RUSTING

10.

Put a four-penny nail through the rivet in the wind vane, then slip a small nut over the end of the nail and hammer the nail into the top of the broomstick.

EARN A BEAR ARROW POINT CREDIT in Wheel Power, Elective 8, by making a weather vane.

Wishing Boats

YOU WILL NEED
Airplane glue
Fingernail polish
Small birthday candles
Scraps of colored construction paper
Tongue depressors (10 cents a dozen
 at the drug store)

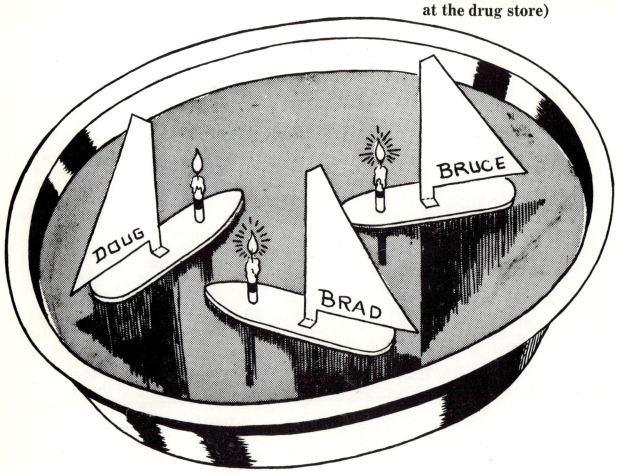

At a birthday party, after the ice cream and cake have been eaten, guests place their boats in a shallow dish of water in the center of the table. As the candles are lighted, each person makes a wish. The person whose candle burns down to the colored line first, will have his wish come true.

**EARN AN ARROW
POINT CREDIT**
in Elective 10 by making wishing boats for each guest at a birthday party.

1.

Whittle a tongue depressor into two boats, like this. Whittle toward the middle to avoid splitting the stick.

2.

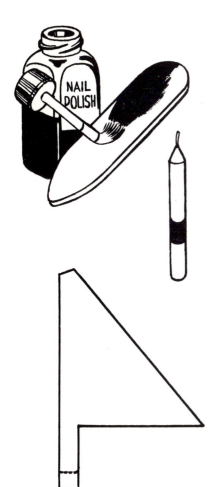

Paint one side of the boat with fingernail polish. When dry, paint the other side and edges.

3.

Paint a narrow band of nail polish around the middle of a birthday candle.

4.

Draw or trace a sail (like pattern at the left) on a piece of colored construction paper, and cut it out. Print your name on the sail.

5.

Mark a square and a circle on the boat (like pattern at the right). These marks show where to put the sail and the candle so the boat will float straight.

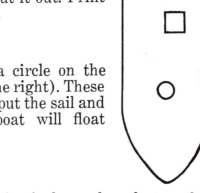

6.

With airplane glue, fasten the sail and the candle to the boat. When the glue has dried, paint a band of nail polish around the bottom of the sail to make it stronger.

7.

A large, wooden wishing boat with a paddle can be used for an after-dark program or ceremony by a lake or pond.

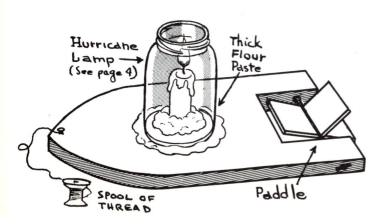

Hurricane Lamp (See page 4)

Thick Flour Paste

SPOOL OF THREAD

Paddle

Finger Puppets

Pictured here are two finger puppets that you can use for giving a puppet show on a table or on the floor. If you want to save these pages in your book, trace the puppets on heavy paper.

1.

Color or paint the puppets before you cut them out.

2.

Attach the puppet to the first two fingers of the hand with a rubber band. Your two fingers are the puppet's legs.

3.

Prop up a mirror on a table so you can see your puppet move as you are practicing. Learn to make the puppet dance, hop, kick, jump, and run.

4.

Put a puppet on each hand. Learn to make the two puppets move together, like a dance team.

5.

You can give a simple puppet show by making your puppets dance to phonograph music.

6.

To make the puppets more real, glue on yarn braids for hair and decorate the costumes with scraps of bright-colored cloth, felt, or feathers. For a most unusual effect, paint the puppets with fluorescent paint and use "black light" to illuminate your show presented in a dark room.

EARN AN ARROW POINT ELECTIVE in Elective 10 by making finger puppets as a party favor.

YOU WILL NEED

**Scissors
Two rubber bands
Paints or crayons**

RUBBER BAND

Photograph a Leaf without a Camera

1.

Arrange leaves on the glass. Use several different kinds and shapes of leaves and grasses to make your picture more interesting.

YOU WILL NEED

A shallow pan
Clip clothespins
A piece of clear glass
Leaves, ferns, and/or grasses
A piece of heavy cardboard the same size as the glass
Architect's blueprint paper (about 25 cents a square yard at a blueprint or architect supply company)

2.

Place blueprint paper the same size as the glass over the leaves with the blue side toward the leaves. In using blueprint paper, the blue side must never be exposed to the light until you are ready to make the photograph.

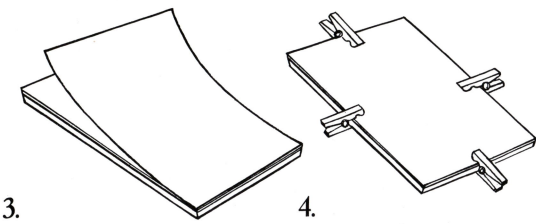

3.

Lay a piece of heavy cardboard over the back side of blueprint paper.

4.

Clip the glass-leaves-blueprint paper-and-heavy cardboard together with clip clothespins.

5.

Expose the blueprint paper to bright sunlight for 1 minute. The blueprint paper will fade white.

6.

Place the blueprint paper in a shallow pan and rinse with running water. The white background will turn blue and the blue leaves, white.

7.

When dry, mount the picture in a scrapbook or in a picture frame.

EARN A BEAR ARROW POINT CREDIT
in Fun with Nature Crafts, Elective 15, by photographing a leaf without a camera.

A terrarium is a little garden sealed in a glass container. Rich soil and moisture inside the jar make the garden grow quickly. In planting the garden, use wild ferns, violets, moss, small cuttings of evergreen, ivy, or any house plant that will grow in water.

How to Make a Small Greenhouse

YOU WILL NEED

A clear, wide-mouth glass gallon jar and lid
    (Ask at your neighborhood grocery, restaurant
    or delicatessen for an empty pickle jar.)
Sand or bird gravel
A piece of burned wood or some charcoal
About two cups of rich garden dirt
Wood to build a base for the jar:
    Plywood, 12 by 8 inches
    Strips of wood ½ inch thick and 1 inch wide
Thin brads or nails
Hammer and a saw
Paint or stain
A variety of plants to place inside the jar

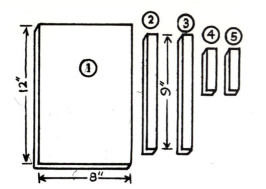
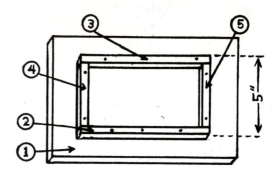

BUILD THE BASE FOR
THE GARDEN FIRST

Five pieces of wood are used to make the base, pictured above. Sandpaper the inside edges of the frame to make the jar fit snugly within it.

NOW PLANT YOUR GARDEN
INSIDE THE JAR

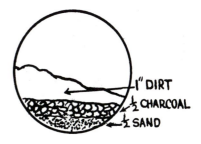

1.

Place the jar, thoroughly clean, on its side on the wooden base.

2.

Put a half-inch layer of sand or bird gravel in the bottom of the jar as it lies on its side.

3.

Crush a piece of charcoal or burned wood between newspapers, and sprinkle a layer of charcoal over the sand.

4.

Add a layer of rich dirt. Garden can be higher at the back side of the jar, but be sure that the dirt is smoothed away from the mouth of the jar so it will not spill out.

5.

Set your plants at least an inch deep in the soil.

6.

Spray the garden with water. Do not get the dirt too wet.

7.

Seal the jar with the lid and set the tiny greenhouse in a spot where it will get some sunlight each day.

8.

Watch the garden carefully for a day or two. If it appears to be too wet, take off the jar lid for a day or more until the garden dries some.

9.

The garden will grow for two or three months without having to be opened.

EARN A WOLF ARROW POINT CREDIT
in Gardener, Elective 17, by making this terrarium.

Make a Catapult

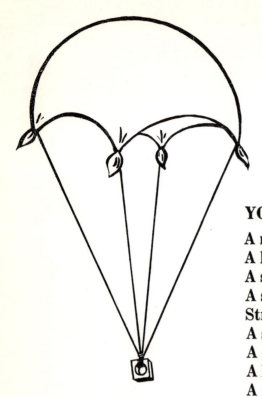

YOU WILL NEED

A nail
A hammer
A small screw
A screw driver
String or heavy thread
A small nut or lightweight washer
A small mustard or pickle jar lid
A lightweight cloth or cleansing tissue about 10 or 12 inches square
A stick of light wood (orange crating is fine) about 18 inches long and 2 inches wide

Airplanes are launched from the deck of a ship with a piece of machinery called a catapult. Here is a simple catapult for launching a parachute.

TO MAKE THE CATAPULT

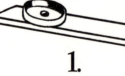

1.

Using a hammer and a nail, punch a hole in the center of a small jar lid. Fasten the lid to the stick of wood with a small screw.

2.

If the screw protrudes through the back side of the stick of wood, slip two or three nuts between the lid and the wood to take up the extra length. That's safety first!

to Launch a Parachute

TO MAKE THE PARACHUTE

3.

Tie a piece of 12-inch string tightly to each corner of a cleansing tissue or lightweight cloth. Then hold the corners of the parachute even, slip the strings through a nut or washer, and tie with a square knot.

4.

Test the parachute by tossing it into the air. If it sails to the ground too fast, the nut is too heavy.

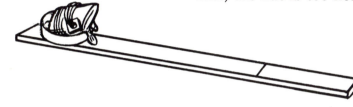

TO LAUNCH THE PARACHUTE

5.

Mark a pencil line across the catapult 6 inches in from the end opposite the jar lid. This is the lever point.

6.

Fold the parachute and wrap the strings loosely around it. Then place the parachute in the jar lid.

7.

Use left hand to hold catapult on porch railing. Strike end of board with right fist.

8.

The parachute will open as it is projected into the air.

EARN AN ARROW POINT CREDIT in Parties and Gifts, Wolf Elective 10, and Machinery, Bear Elective 9, by making a toy catapult to launch a parachute.

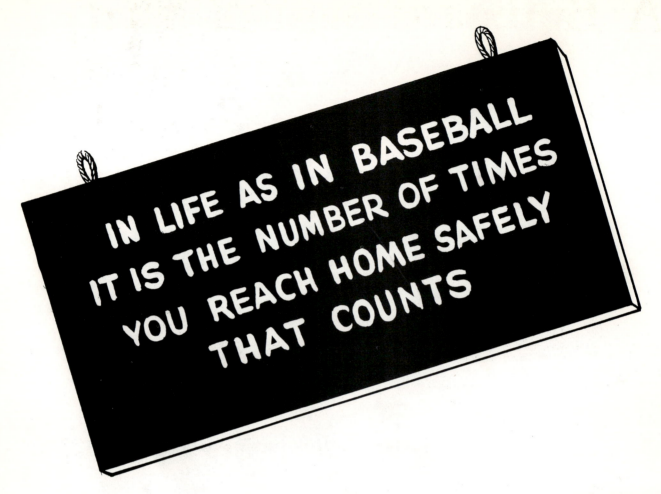

IN LIFE AS IN BASEBALL
IT IS THE NUMBER OF TIMES
YOU REACH HOME SAFELY
THAT COUNTS

1.

Paint or stain a piece of plywood or corrugated cardboard and lay it aside to dry.

2.

Pour some of the alphabet macaroni into a plate. Pick out the letters you need for this sign:

IN LIFE AS IN BASEBALL
IT IS THE NUMBER OF TIMES
YOU REACH HOME SAFELY
THAT COUNTS

A Billboard Sign of Safety

YOU WILL NEED

A plate
Airplane glue
Wood stain or paint
A piece of heavy string about 6 inches long
A package of alphabet macaroni from the grocery store
A piece of plywood or corrugated cardboard about 6 by 8 inches

3.

When the painted board is dry, mark the board lightly with four pencil lines about an inch apart.

4.

Space the words of the sign along the pencil lines. Use only a tiny bit of glue on each letter and press firmly into place.

5.

Glue two loops of string or cord on the back side, top edge, for hangers. Use a lot of glue and let dry.

6.

Shellac your sign to make it last longer.

**EARN A WOLF ARROW
POINT CREDIT**
in Handicraft, Elective 3, by making this billboard safety sign for your school or your home.

Jigsaw Puzzle Greeting Card

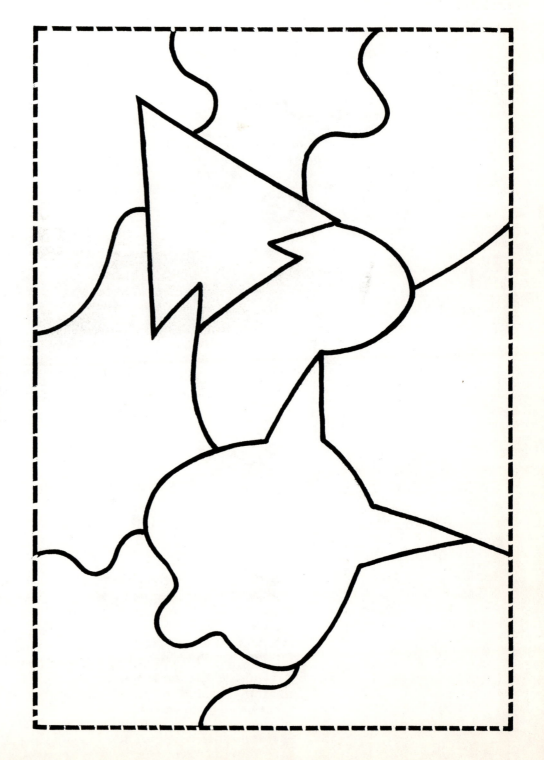

1.

Trace this jigsaw puzzle pattern on a piece of heavy paper and trim the puzzle along dotted line.

BLANK SIDE OF HEAVY PAPER

PASTE ON PICTURE AND LETTERING

JIGSAW PUZZLE TRACED ON THE BACK

SIGN YOUR NAME HERE

HURRY UP Get WELL SOON

Jack Jones

2.

Cut a small colored picture about 4 inches wide, 3 inches high, from a magazine.

3.

Cut letters from magazines to spell "Hurry Up—Get Well Soon," or other greetings.

4.

Paste the picture and letters on the blank side of the heavy paper, as shown here.

5.

Put your card between sheets of clean paper and place under a heavy book to dry.

6.

When the paste is dry, sign your name on the card. Then cut the card into pieces, following the pattern of the jigsaw on the back side.

7.

Address an envelope for mailing. Count the ten pieces of the puzzle as you put them into the envelope.

EARN A WOLF ARROW POINT CREDIT in Parties and Gifts, Elective 10, by making a jigsaw puzzle greeting card to mail to a friend or relative.

Pirate  Gold

EARN A WOLF ARROW POINT CREDIT
in Parties and Gifts, Elective 10, by making a gift
of the Pirate Gold game. See instructions on page 20.

YOU WILL NEED

A matchstick to follow the route

1.

The object of the game is to go from
the pirate ship to the buried treasure
by following the compass directions
along the route.

2.

First, study the compass on the map
and learn the directions in relation to
the page:

    North is up—toward the top of the
        page

    South is down—toward the bottom
        of the page

    East is across—toward the right
        side of the page

    West is across—toward the left
        side of the page

3.

Start from the ship. Follow the path
with a matchstick. By following the
directions along the route you will
make the shortest and fastest jour-
ney to the buried treasure.

How to Make a Rain Gauge

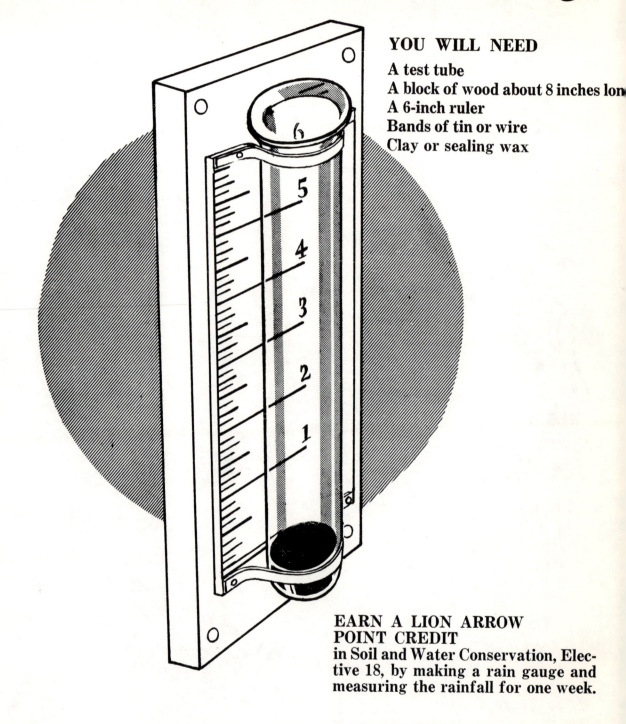

YOU WILL NEED

A test tube
A block of wood about 8 inches lon
A 6-inch ruler
Bands of tin or wire
Clay or sealing wax

**EARN A LION ARROW
POINT CREDIT**
in Soil and Water Conservation, Elective 18, by making a rain gauge and measuring the rainfall for one week.

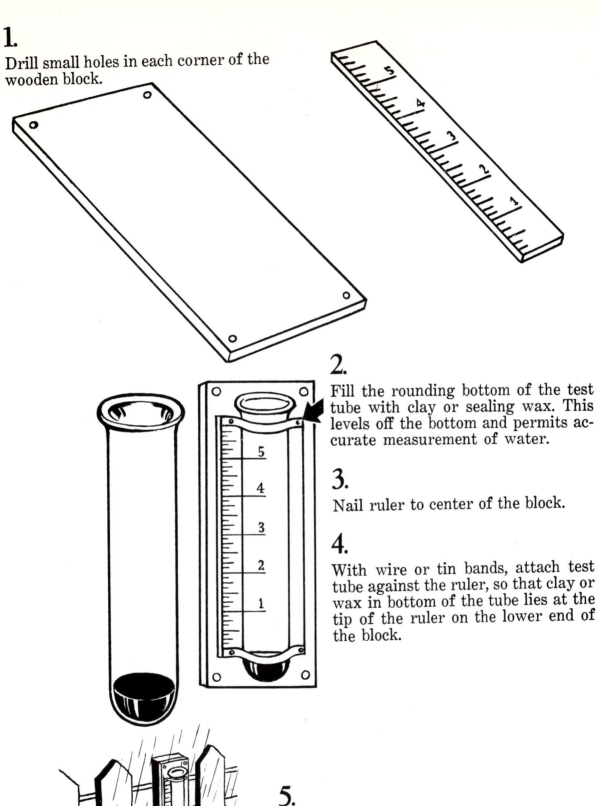

1.

Drill small holes in each corner of the wooden block.

2.

Fill the rounding bottom of the test tube with clay or sealing wax. This levels off the bottom and permits accurate measurement of water.

3.

Nail ruler to center of the block.

4.

With wire or tin bands, attach test tube against the ruler, so that clay or wax in bottom of the tube lies at the tip of the ruler on the lower end of the block.

5.

Fasten the rain gauge to a fence or post, in an open area, away from buildings or trees. After each rain, read the gauge to see how much water fell, then empty the tube and set back into place.

Bird Feeders

YOU WILL NEED

Three large screw eyes
A piece of wire
A brace and bits to drill ¼ inch and ¾ inch holes
A small log about 10 inches long
¼ inch dowel or small sticks
A two-by-four piece of wood 10 inches long
Some evergreen twigs

Birds do not like the smell of paint, so leave the feeders unpainted. Do not hang feeder against the house. Birds will flock to a bird feeder during cold weather when other food is scarce. Fill the holes in the feeder regularly with peanut butter or beef suet. Remember, too, to set out a pan of water for them.

1.

Put a screw eye in the top center of a 10-inch log.

2.

Use a brace and ¾-inch bit to drill 4 holes, ½ inch deep, as pictured. Holes should be staggered.

3.

Holes slant downward.

4.

Hang feeder from a tree with wire, where you can watch your bird visitors often.

BIRD FEEDER NO. 2

1.
Put two screw eyes in the top of a 10-inch piece of two-by-four wood.

2.
Drill four holes, ½ inch deep, ¾ inch wide, as pictured.

3.
One inch below each food hole, drill a ¼-inch hole for perch.

4.
Drill ¼-inch holes in both sides, insert evergreen twigs for extra attraction to the birds.

5.
Food holes and perch holes slant downward.

6.
Perches are made of dowel stick, or from straight twigs.

7.
Hang feeder from a tree so cats cannot bother the birds while they are eating.

EARN A WOLF ARROW POINT CREDIT
in Handicraft, Elective 3, by making one or both of these bird feeders to attract birds to your yard.

An Airplane with Lifting Power

YOU WILL NEED

A pencil
Scissors
A sheet of tablet or typing paper

① Fold a sheet of typing paper on a diagonal, as shown.

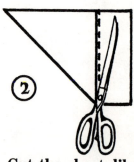

② Cut the sheet, like this.

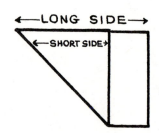

③ Letter the strip, X, and the triangle, A.

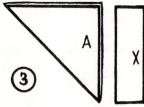

④ Fold strip X in half.

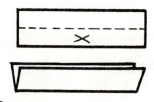
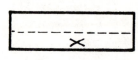
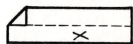
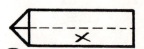

⑤ Open strip X and fold one end into a point, like this.

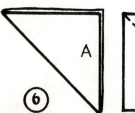

⑥ Open piece A and mark the inside of the paper B.

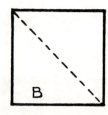
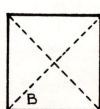

⑦ With B side up, fold the paper to make two diagonal creases, as shown.

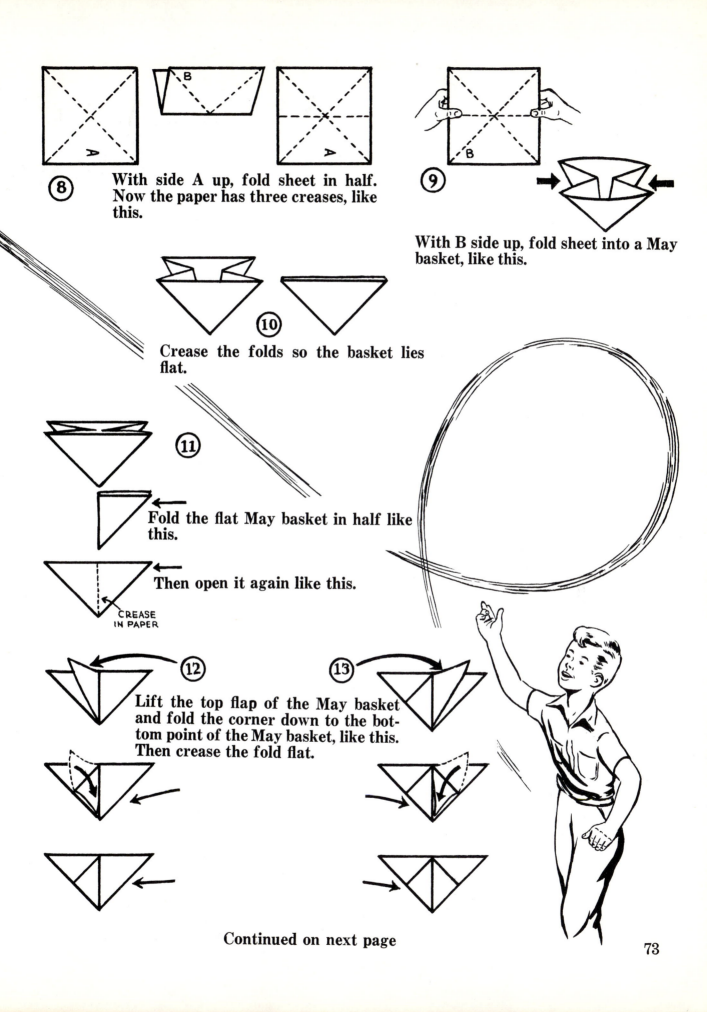

8 With side A up, fold sheet in half. Now the paper has three creases, like this.

9 With B side up, fold sheet into a May basket, like this.

10 Crease the folds so the basket lies flat.

11 Fold the flat May basket in half like this.

Then open it again like this.

CREASE IN PAPER

12 Lift the top flap of the May basket and fold the corner down to the bottom point of the May basket, like this. Then crease the fold flat.

13

Continued on next page

73

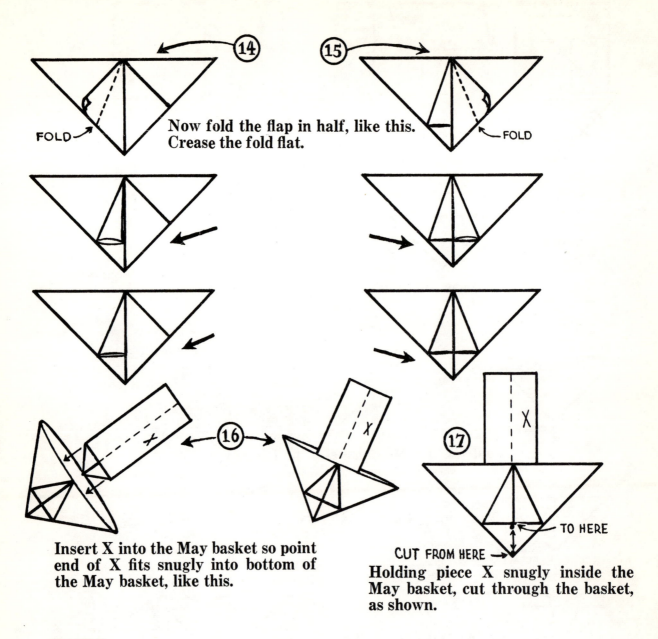

Now fold the flap in half, like this. Crease the fold flat.

⑯

Insert X into the May basket so point end of X fits snugly into bottom of the May basket, like this.

⑰

CUT FROM HERE → → TO HERE

Holding piece X snugly inside the May basket, cut through the basket, as shown.

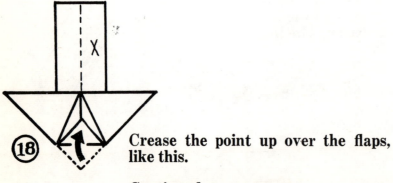

⑱ Crease the point up over the flaps, like this.

Continued on next page

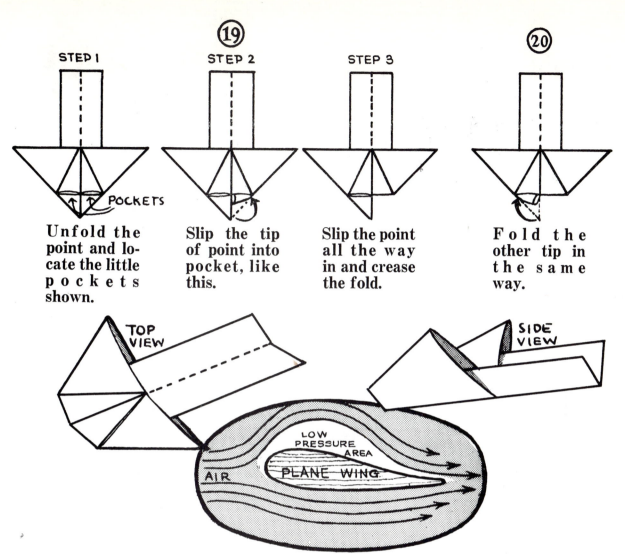

⑲

STEP 1

Unfold the point and locate the little pockets shown.

STEP 2

Slip the tip of point into pocket, like this.

STEP 3

Slip the point all the way in and crease the fold.

⑳

Fold the other tip in the same way.

You now have an airplane with wing foil, similar to a real plane. As plane sails through the air, the curvature of the wings develops a low pressure area on top side of wings. (See illustration.) Air below pushes up on bottom side of wings to equalize the air pressures, causing plane to rise.

Hold plane by the nose or laced in your three center fingers. Throw plane above your head and watch it sail.

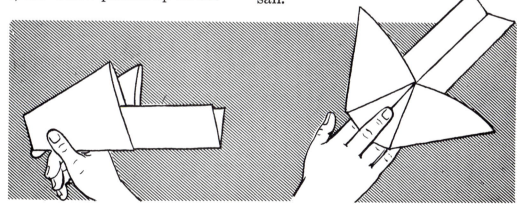

EARN A WOLF ARROW POINT CREDIT
in Parties and Gifts, Elective 10, by making this paper toy airplane with wings that have lifting power. You may want to give it to a friend.

How to Make a Tambourine

NAIL

HAMMER

POP
12
BOTTLE CAPS

ICE
ICE PICK

LARGE
DARNING
NEEDLE

4
PAPER PLATES

YARN,
HEAVY STRING,
OR PLASTIC GIMP

COLORED RIBBON
OR FEATHERS

YOU WILL NEED
(Items needed are pictured on drawing)

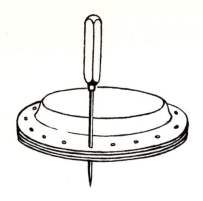

KNOT STRING HERE

1.

Set four heavy paper plates one inside the other. Punch holes, 1½ inches apart, around the rim of the plates.

2.

Place two plates (one inside the other) face to face with the other two plates. Lace and tie the plates together with yarn, heavy string, cord, plastic gimp, or craftstrip.

3.

With a nail and hammer, punch holes in the centers of twelve pop bottle caps. String the bottle caps—four to a group—on heavy string or cord. Tie groups of bottle caps to the tambourine so they will jingle.

4.

Paint or color the tambourine with bright designs. Then tie streamers of ribbon or feathers to the rim as the final decoration.

5.

Shake the tambourine and beat it with a closed fist.

**EARN A BEAR ARROW
POINT CREDIT**

in Cub Scout Band, Elective 12, by making and learning to play a tambourine.

A Shadow Puppet

YOU WILL NEED

Scissors
Paste or a stapler
A sheet of tissue paper or very thin paper
A piece of heavy wrapping paper or construction paper
A piece of medium-weight cardboard about 8½ by 11 inches

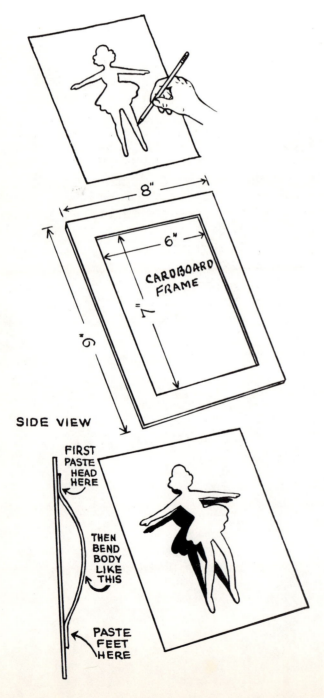

This shadow puppet always brings a laugh from your audience. It's a good stunt for a pack meeting or for a party, and it makes a clever gift for a sick-abed friend.

1.

Trace the pattern of the dancer on a piece of heavy wrapping paper or construction paper and cut out.

2.

Make a frame of light cardboard about 9 inches high and 8 inches wide. Center opening in the cardboard is 7 inches high, 6 inches wide.

3.

Fasten the puppet to a sheet of thin paper so dancer bends out from the paper. Paste or staple the puppet as shown.

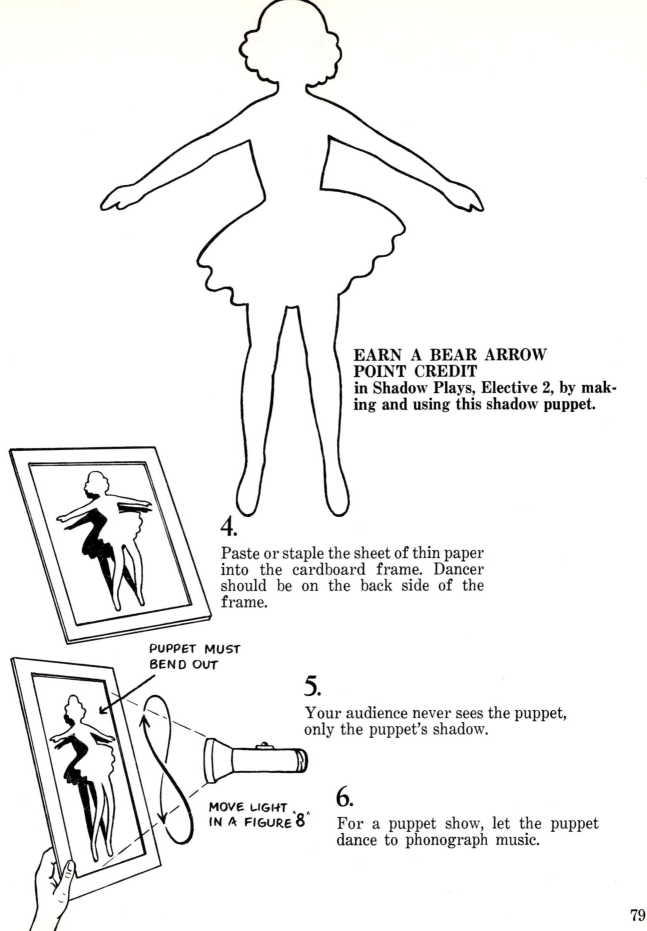

**EARN A BEAR ARROW
POINT CREDIT**
in Shadow Plays, Elective 2, by making and using this shadow puppet.

4.

Paste or staple the sheet of thin paper into the cardboard frame. Dancer should be on the back side of the frame.

PUPPET MUST
BEND OUT

5.

Your audience never sees the puppet, only the puppet's shadow.

MOVE LIGHT
IN A FIGURE "8"

6.

For a puppet show, let the puppet dance to phonograph music.

A Flying Fish
for Kite Fans

This fancy kite takes a lot of work and ingenuity, but you and your dad will be well rewarded for the effort when you see it soaring high in the sky like a flying fish.

YOU WILL NEED

Two dowel sticks, both about 3 feet long, ¼ inch thick

Two long pieces of basketmaker's reed

(One piece should be about 8-9 feet long, the other about 5-6 feet long.)

Strips of cloth for the tail

Varied-color water paints for decorating the kite

Paste or uncooked egg whites for gluing

Very fine, lightweight wire

Ball of strong string

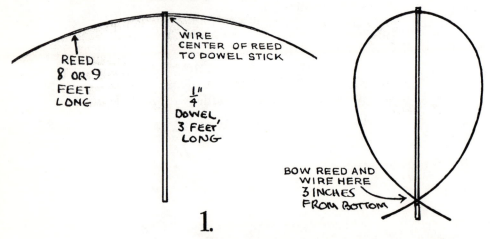

1.

Wire a 9-foot length of basketmaker's reed to the top of a 3-foot dowel stick. Then bend each end of the reed, as shown, and wire to dowel 3 inches from the bottom.

EARN A WOLF ARROW POINT CREDIT
in Kites, Elective 7, by making this handsome fish kite.

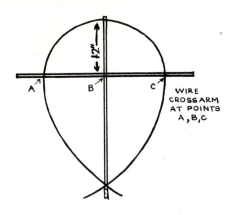

2.

Wire the second dowel stick into the cross-arm position, as shown.

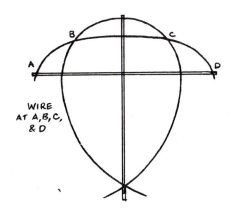

4.

Bow reed as shown, and wire at points A, B, C, and D.

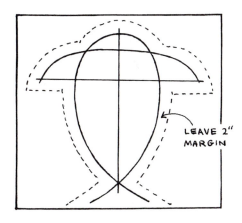

6.

Use the frame to mark pattern on thin kite paper, leaving a 2-inch edge of paper for gluing.

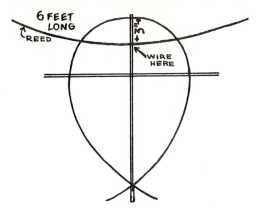

3.

Wire a 6-foot reed to the center dowel stick, 3 or 4 inches from the top of the kite.

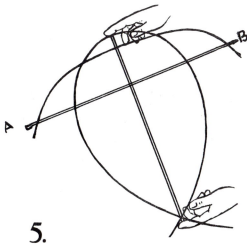

5.

Balance the kite frame by resting the top and the bottom of the upright dowel stick on finger tips. Trim ends of dowel and reeds at point A or B to get perfect balance.

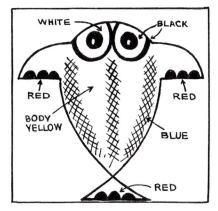

7.

Before cutting the paper, paint the kite like a flying fish. Paint will make paper shrink a little.

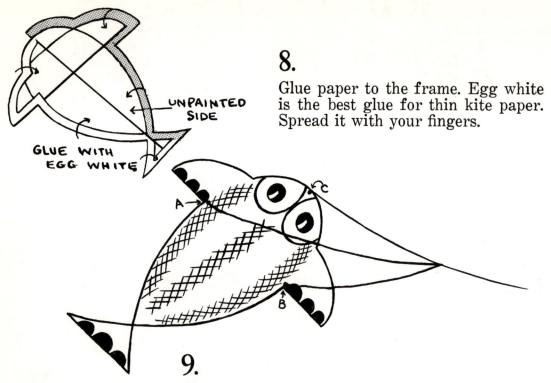

GLUE WITH
EGG WHITE

UNPAINTED
SIDE

8.

Glue paper to the frame. Egg white is the best glue for thin kite paper. Spread it with your fingers.

9.

Bridle the kite from points A, B, and C. The bridle hangs on the painted side of the kite. If, at first, this particular bridle-tie does not work, readjust it or retie from different positions until you find the balance points for flying.

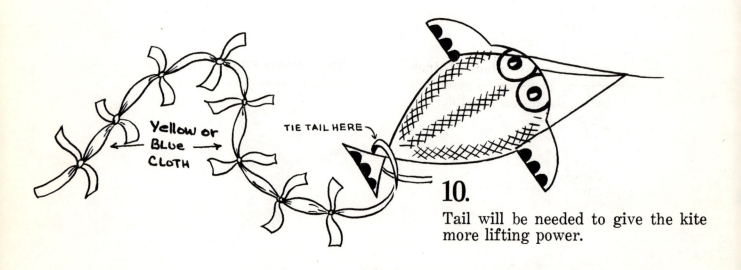

Yellow or
Blue
Cloth

TIE TAIL HERE

10.

Tail will be needed to give the kite more lifting power.

Star Tricks

YOU WILL NEED

Scissors
A pencil
Several pieces of blank paper

Here are some tricky ways of making stars. The first design is made without lifting your pencil from the paper.

1.
First draw a "V"

2.
Now cross the "T"

3.
Straight to the right

4.
And the star shines bright!

Can you make a five-pointed star from a straight strip of paper? It's an interesting trick.

1.

Cut a strip of paper about 1 inch wide and 8 inches long. The edges should be as straight as possible.

2.

Tie a single knot in the center of the strip of paper.

3.
Carefully pull the knot tight, then press it flat.

4.
CUT HERE

Cut off the ends of the piece of paper as shown.

5.
Lay the knot on a piece of paper and draw round it. This is the center of the star.

6.
With a ruler, extend lines from each edge of the center design and you will have a five-pointed star.

Make Water Rise

YOU WILL NEED

A plate
A match
A water glass
A scrap of paper
A small piece of cardboard

1.

Pour a little water on a plate.

2.

Float a small piece of heavy cardboard on the water and place a scrap of newspaper on the cardboard.

3.

Light the scrap of newspaper and cover the flame with a glass.

4.

As long as the fire burns, water will rise slowly up into the glass.

into a Glass

THIS IS WHAT HAPPENS

It is fun to think a battle is taking place when water rises into the glass. It really is a battle between Fire, Water, and Air.

When you set the glass over Fire, a glassful of Air—which we shall call "Inside Air"—is trapped in the glass with Fire. Water around the rim of the glass locks (or seals) Fire and Inside Air in the glass.

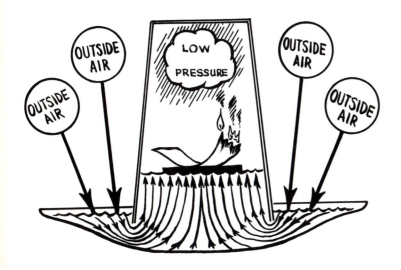

As Fire burns, it uses oxygen in the Air. Therefore, Inside Air becomes weaker—has a lower pressure—as Fire takes oxygen from it.

Outside Air—the air outside the glass —tries to rush into the glass to fill the low-pressure area, but Water is in its way. Pushed by Outside Air, Water is forced up into the glass to fill the low-pressure area.

When Fire has used all the oxygen in Inside Air, the battle is over. Fire dies. Water is trapped inside the glass. Outside Air is the winner.

The Betsy Ross Star

YOU WILL NEED

A pair of scissors
A 4-inch square of very thin paper

In 1776, General George Washington and a group of his friends asked Betsy Ross to make a flag they had designed for the new United States. The flag had 13 stripes and 13 stars —one stripe and one star for each of the states. The stars were six-pointed stars. With a few quick folds of a piece of cloth and with one snip of her scissors, Betsy Ross showed General Washington that it was easier and faster to make stars with five points. This is how Betsy did it. The only difficulty in making a perfect star is in learning how to fold the paper. Use very thin paper—it's easier to fold.

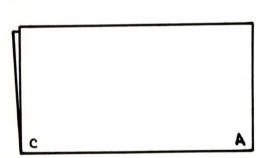

1.

Fold a 4-inch square of very thin paper in half and lay it on the table with the folded edge toward you.

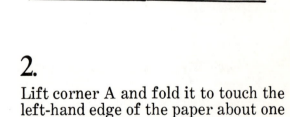

2.

Lift corner A and fold it to touch the left-hand edge of the paper about one third the distance from the top to the bottom.

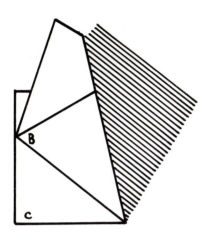

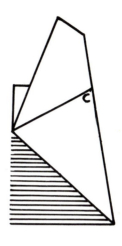

3.

Lift corner B and fold it to touch corner A. Crease the folds with your fingernail to make the paper lie flat.

4.

Lift corner C and fold it over the other folds of paper. Crease the fold with your fingernail.

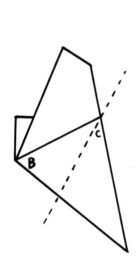

5.

With your scissors, make one snip across the folded paper as shown by the dotted line.

6.

Now unfold the small triangle and you'll find a five-pointed "Betsy Ross" star.

Button Button

YOU WILL NEED

Five buttons

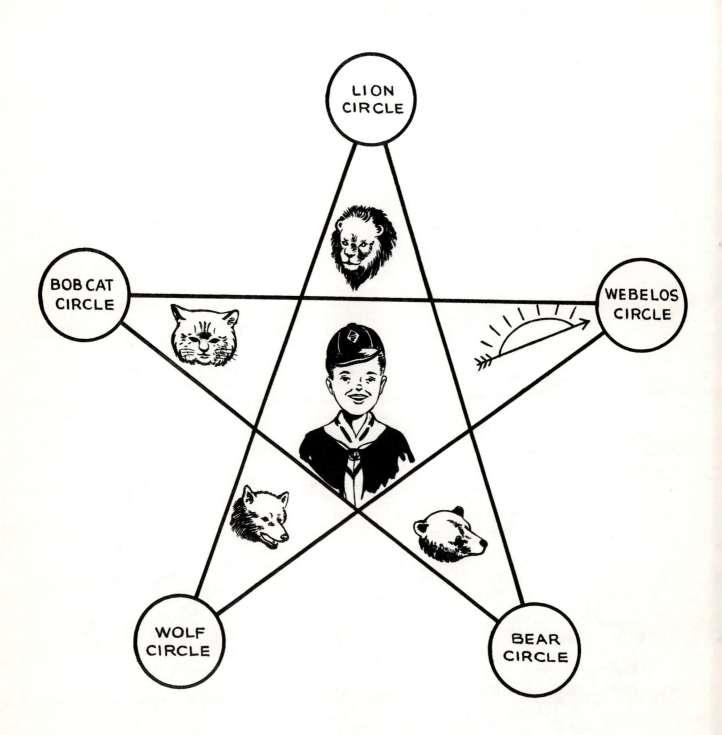

The object of this puzzle is to fill all the circles on the points of the star with buttons, in this way:

1.

First, place a button in any circle and slide it across the star, following one of the straight lines, to another open circle.

2.

After a button has been moved across the star, it cannot be moved again.

3.

No more than one button can occupy a circle.

4.

Move the second, third, and fourth buttons, one by one, in the same manner as you did the first.

5.

The fifth button is placed directly in the only remaining open circle.

HERE'S HOW IT'S DONE

If your first button was moved from Lion circle to the Bear circle, then your second button must be moved to fill the Lion circle, etc. The trick is to slide the button to the circle that was last used as a starting point.

EARN A WOLF ARROW POINT CREDIT
in Parties and Gifts, Elective 10, by mounting this puzzle and the instructions on a card and mailing it with five buttons to a sick-abed friend. He'll enjoy trying to work it.

Boomerang!

Boomerang!

YOU WILL NEED

Scissors
A pencil
A piece of cardboard
A sheet of carbon paper
A book larger than the boomerang

This boomerang is a simple one, but it will work exactly like the boomerangs used by natives of Australia, South Africa, and India. You can make it whirl across the room and return to the spot from which you threw it.

1.

Trace the boomerang pattern on a piece of stiff cardboard and cut it out.

2.

Lay the boomerang on a book or magazine with one prong extending over the side of the book.

3.

Tip the front of the book up a little and hit the prong of the boomerang with a quick forward stroke of a pencil.

4.

If you hit it correctly, the boomerang will whirl out across the room and return to the spot where you are standing.

90

EARN A WOLF ARROW POINT CREDIT
in Parties and Gifts, Elective 10, by making a boomerang for a gift.

A Spinning Color Wheel

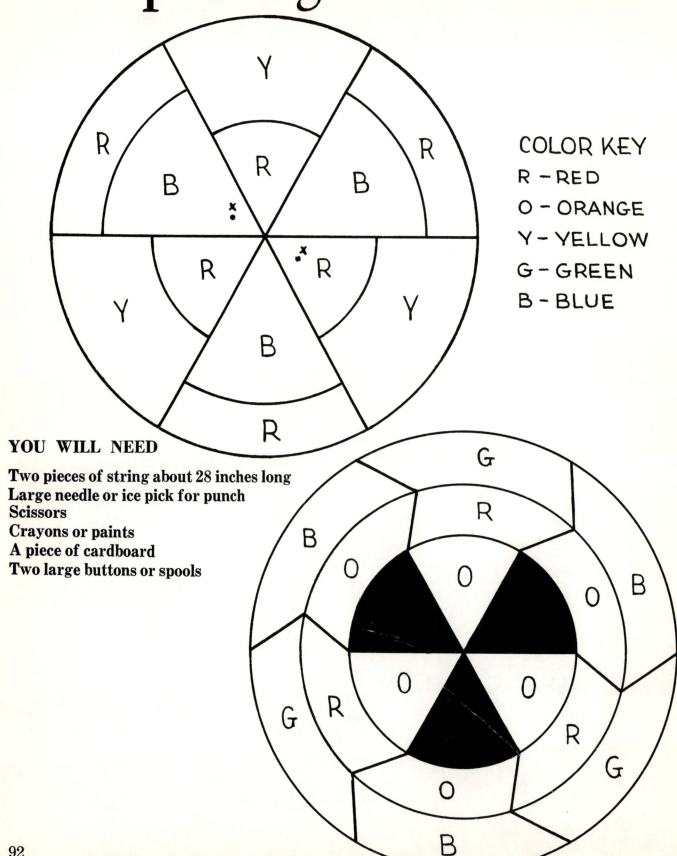

COLOR KEY
R – RED
O – ORANGE
Y – YELLOW
G – GREEN
B – BLUE

YOU WILL NEED

Two pieces of string about 28 inches long
Large needle or ice pick for punch
Scissors
Crayons or paints
A piece of cardboard
Two large buttons or spools

TO MAKE THE WHEEL

1.

Cut out a heavy cardboard wheel, the size of the wheels on the opposite page.

2.

Color or paint the two sides of the wheel, using colors and design indicated.

3.

At each point marked "X" on one side of the color wheel, punch a hole with a large needle or ice pick.

4.

Thread pieces of string through each of the holes.

5.

Thread the string ends through large buttons or spools (for handles) and tie.

TO OPERATE THE WHEEL

1.

Gripping the color wheel by the handles, whirl the wheel around and around until the string is well twisted.

2.

Now pull out slowly on the handles so that the wheel begins to whirl as the string untwists.

3.

When the wheel has started to spin rapidly, let the strings hang slightly loose. The wheel will continue to spin until it winds the string in the opposite direction. Now you are ready to pull out slowly on the handles again, etc.

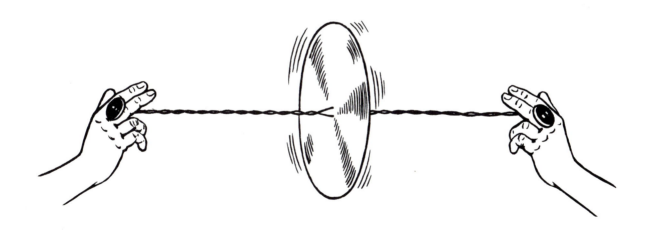

EARN A WOLF ARROW POINT CREDIT in Parties and Gifts, Elective 10, by making a color-wheel toy for a friend.

Fun with an Ant House

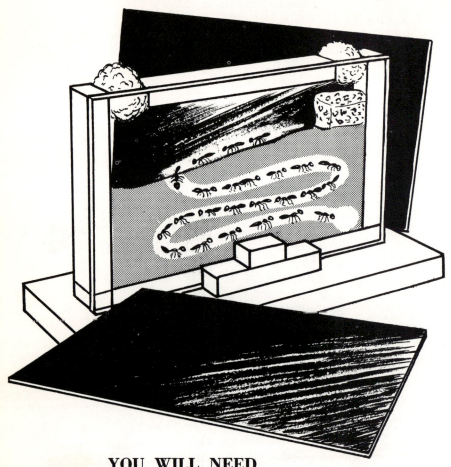

If you can find an anthill in your yard or garden, you'll have the "time of your life" with an ant house. The house is nothing more than a "sandwich" made from two pieces of glass, with ants and dirt in between. Every day you can watch the ants at work in their glass house. Materials for the ant house will cost less than a dollar. You'll probably need your dad's help building it.

YOU WILL NEED

Two panes of glass, 8 by 10 inches or larger, from old picture frames or cut to size at a hardware store

Some strips of wood about ½ inch wide and ½ inch thick and the end of an orange crate or similar wood

A roll of adhesive tape or black tape, 1 inch wide

A piece of sponge about 1 inch wide, 1 inch high, and ½ inch thick

A hammer and some long, thin nails or brads

Two pieces of cardboard cut to the size of the panes of glass

Airplane glue

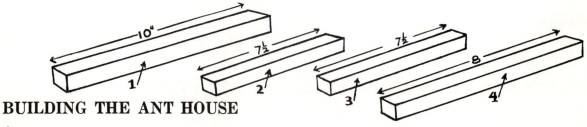

BUILDING THE ANT HOUSE

1.

Cut four strips of wood, ½ inch wide and ½ inch thick to the sizes pictured here.

94

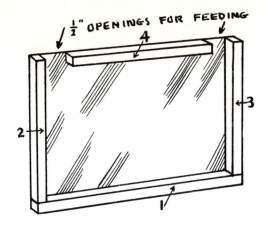

NOW FOR THE FUN

1.

Dig up the colony of ants. Be sure you get the queen ant—an ant much larger than the others—for the colony of ants must have a queen.

2.

Put the ants inside the frame; then fill the frame more than half full with dirt.

3.

Place the piece of sponge on top of the dirt, near one of the air holes in the top of the frame.

2.

Lay one pane of glass on a table and glue the strips of wood to it. Use airplane glue.

4.

Quickly glue the other pane of glass to the wooden frame.

5.

Plug the two air holes with cotton so the ants cannot escape.

6.

Tape the edges of the glass "sandwich" with adhesive tape. *Do not tape over the air holes.*

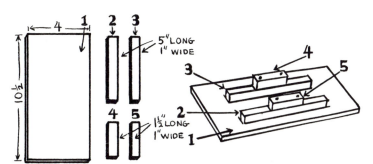

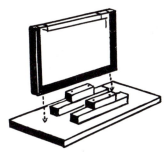

TO MAKE A STAND FOR THE ANT HOUSE

1.

Use an orange crate or similar wood and thin nails for the base.

2.

The ant house will stand upright between the strips of wood nailed to the base.

TO CARE FOR YOUR ANTS

1.

Saturate the sponge in the ant house with water at least once a week. Use an eyedropper. The dirt in the house should be moist but not wet. Too much water will drown the ants.

2.

Feed the ants every few days. A drop of honey or molasses, tiny bits of mashed nuts, apples, or bananas will do. Ants do not need much food. Avoid overfeeding.

3.

Keep the ant house away from bright sunlight and heat pipes.

4.

Ants like to work in the dark. When you are not watching them, cover the sides of the glass house with cardboard to keep their home dark.

**EARN A LION ARROW
POINT CREDIT
in Nature, Elective 15, by making an
ant house and keeping some ants in it.**